DRAGONFLIES
OF THE FLORIDA PENINSULA, BERMUDA, AND THE BAHAMAS

D1452927

SCIENTIFIC PUBLISHERS NATURE GUIDES

1. Dragonflies of the Florida Peninsula, Bermuda, and the Bahamas — S. W. Dunkle

In Preparation:

Butterflies of California
    [facsimile reprint]
    J. A. Comstock
    Introduction by T.C. & J.F. Emmel

Peruvian Jungle Insects

Natural Areas of Florida

Day-flying Moths of Taiwan

Damselflies of Florida

Birds of Florida

DRAGONFLIES
OF THE FLORIDA PENINSULA, BERMUDA, AND THE BAHAMAS

by
Sidney W. Dunkle, Ph.D.

Manager
International Odonata Research Institute
Gainesville, Florida

Research Associate
Florida State Collection of Arthropods
Gainesville, Florida

SCIENTIFIC PUBLISHERS
Gainesville - Washington

1989

THE SANDHILL CRANE PRESS, INC.
2406 NW 47th Terrace
GAINESVILLE, FL 32606
(904) 371-9858

Library of Congress Cataloging-in-Publication Data
Dunkle, Sidney W.
    Dragonflies of the Florida peninsula, Bermuda, and the Bahamas / by
Sidney W. Dunkle.
        x, 155 p.; 23 cm.
        Bibliography: p. 147
        Includes index.
        1. Dragonflies--Florida. 2. Dragonflies--Bahamas.
    3. Dragonflies--Bermuda Islands. 4. Insects--Florida. 5.Insects-
    -Bahamas. 6. Insects--Bermuda Islands.   I. Title.
    QL520.2.U6D86   1989
    595.7'3309759--dc19   88-38269
                                                             CIP

ISBN 0-945417-23-3
Printed in the United States of America
10 9 8 7 6 5 4 3 2 1

Cover: The face of the Swamp Darner (*Epiaeschna heros*), the last thing millions of mosquitos see every year!

DEDICATION

For Isabell, Maynard, Kay, and Bruce,
who have always stood
behind me 101%

PREFACE

Dragonflies are special animals. They attract attention by their double-winged symmetry, intricate coloration, and incredible aerobatic skills, all of which are readily seen near almost any body of water. In fact it is quite easy to use binoculars to identify and watch dragonflies at a distance, as in bird watching. Another of their attractions is that they can not harm humans in any way; they do not sting, and their bite when held in the hand is no more than a pinch. Their bite is much more severe to the mosquitoes, flies, gnats, and numerous other pestiferous insects that they eat. A common name for them in Florida is "mosquito hawk," which aptly describes their habits.

Dragonflies have habits which are discussed later in this book that are practically unique among animals. For example, a male dragonfly must "mate" with himself before he can mate with a female! Also the larvae are unique at both ends—they catch prey with a large arm-like lower lip, and their gills are located in their rectum!

This is the first color guide to the dragonflies of any part of North America. It includes all of the 94 species that have been found in the Florida Peninsula, Bermuda, and the Bahama Islands. Photographs of most of these species have not been published previously. The book is a useful aid for identifying dragonflies in any part of the United States and Canada, for it includes about a third of the species occurring in North America.

I hope that you have even part of the fun I have had watching dragonflies over the years. If you get interested enough in dragonflies to help preserve some of Florida's wetland habitats for them and for other wildlife, I will feel well satisfied in taking the time to write this book.

I warmly thank G. Bick, J. Bick, J. Heppner, H. Nadel, and P. Sohler for critiquing an early draft of the manuscript.

TABLE OF CONTENTS

INTRODUCTION

How the Species Accounts are Organized in this Book

Information on each species is placed in 3 major categories: Identification, Ecology, and Behavior. Under Identification the total body length, from the face to the tip of the terminal abdominal appendages, is given in millimeters (and in inches in parentheses). Note that millimeters and inches are easily interconverted because 25 mm = 1 inch. Dragonflies in this book range from 25 to 100 mm (i.e. 1 to 4 in) long, rather loosely grouped into the categories very small, small, medium, fairly large, large, and very large. If the species is found only in the northern half of the Florida Peninsula, or only in the southern half, that distribution is noted. The general subjective status of the species in the Florida Peninsula is given in the following increasing categories: Vagrant, Rare, Scarce, Uncommon, Common, or Abundant. If there are other species that might be particularly confused with the species under discussion, differences among them are given in a separate paragraph in the Identification section.

In the Ecology section are placed data on geographical distribution, breeding habitat, and flight season. The distribution is first given for Florida, and then for the rest of the species' range. If the species has been found in the Florida Keys or in the Dry Tortugas Islands, this is specifically stated. Flowing water habitats are given in increasing size as: Seepages, Trickles, Rivulets, Streams, and Rivers. These habitats are not sharply defined, but streams are here considered to be wide enough when bordered by trees to receive direct sunlight for part of the day. The ditches and canals of southern Florida have little flow and are habitats of pond species. Lakes are here considered to be different from ponds if they are large enough for some wave action and thus are better oxygenated. Some river species breed in lakes due to the open shoreline and wave motion. While pond species can breed in lakes, some lake species cannot survive in ponds. Borrow Pits are ponds made when soil or rock is "borrowed" for fill during construction projects. Such ponds, when newly created, are the habitat of species which are not good competitors in long established habitats. Marshes, often called Wet Prairies in Florida, are shallow bodies of water with emergent herbaceous plants such as grass, cattails, or pickerel weed. The Everglades is a slowly flowing marshy river. Swamps are shallow water bodies with emergent trees such as Bald Cypress or Tupelo Gum. Bogs are ponds or seepages dominated by Sphagnum Moss which makes the water more acidic. Bogs are special places with many uncommon plants and animals which can not compete well with organisms in other habitats. Generally the flight season is longest in southern Florida, but it varies with the weather from year to year. Species which might fly all year in a warm winter have a shorter flight season in a winter with early or late frosts. In December and January, few adult dragonflies are seen even in southern Florida.

In the Behavior section data are given on perching sites and postures, feeding, maturation areas away from water, territorial behavior, mating, and oviposition (egg laying). Much of the information in this book is from personal observations of the author, but data were extracted from every available source. I felt that it was not appropriate in a book of this kind to cite the origin of every fact, but those studies concentrating on a particular species are listed as sources and for further reading. In a few cases I have given a favorite quote which seems to capture the essence of a species in its natural setting.

What is a Dragonfly?

Dragonflies are insects, with the body supported by a shell- like outer skeleton (exoskeleton), and with jointed legs. Like most other insects they have 3 body regions, including a head which bears 2 antennae, a thorax which bears 4 wings and 6 legs, and an abdomen with 2 or 3 terminal appendages at its tip.

Fig. 1. Clean, sand-bottomed Florida stream, habitat of many scarce dragonfly species, especially Clubtails. The water is stained to the "blackwater" condition due to the tannin leached from tree roots and decaying leaves.

Fig. 2. Clear-water, sand-bottomed lake margined with Maiden Cane grass, habitat of 3 dragonfly species endemic to Florida.

Dragonflies belong to one large group, or Order, of insects called the Odonata ("the toothed ones"). Examples of other insect Orders are the Diptera, the true flies, and the Hemiptera, the true bugs. Odonata are easily differentiated from other insects by the combination of 4 equal-length cellophane-like wings, and tiny bristle-like antennae. The Order Odonata includes 2 Suborders found in Florida, the Anisoptera ("unequal wings") or Dragonflies, and the Zygoptera ("similar wings") or Damselflies. The Dragonflies are generally larger and stouter than the Damselflies, their hindwings are broader at the base than the forewings, and the eyes are often so large that they touch on top of the head. In Damselflies, the fore- and hindwings are similar in shape, and their eyes are always widely separated. During mating, male Dragonflies grasp the female's head with 3 terminal abdominal appendages, male Damselflies grasp the female's thorax with 4 such appendages. Finally, Florida Dragonflies are easily told from Damselflies by their wing position when perched. Dragonflies perch with the wings straight out to the sides, although a few species cock them downward or allow the wind to lift them upward. Most Damselflies perch with the wings pressed together over their back; a few hold them partly spread. Dragonfly larvae differ from Damselfly larvae most notably at the rear end, where Dragonflies have stout pointed terminal appendages but Damselflies have 3 leaf- like gills.

The insects most similar to the adult Odonata are in the Order Neuroptera, the Owlflies and Antlions, but these fold their wings roof-like over their abdomens, and have club-shaped antennae. The larvae of Odonata differ from those of all other insects by their greatly enlarged lower lip, which is used for capturing prey.

Naming and Classifying Dragonflies

The "common names" used in this book are not common names but rather English names, because the general public has not distinguished different species of dragonflies with different names. Most of the English names in this book were invented by the author and by Dennis R. Paulson. We tried to construct an integrated set of concise and descriptive names. Most scientists will not know these English names, so if you communicate with scientists about dragonflies, use the scientific names.

Scientific names basically consist of two words, which are either italicized or underlined to make them stand out from the rest of a text. The first word is capitalized and is called the genus ("jeen-us"), the second word is not capitalized and is called the species ("spee-sees") adjective. The species adjective is not properly used alone, and both words are required to make the scientific name. An example of a scientific name is that of the Sandhill Clubtail, *Gomphus cavillaris*, with *Gomphus* being the genus and *cavillaris* the specific adjective. Generally a genus is a group containing 2 or more similar species, but sometimes a species is considered so different from any other that it is given a genus by itself. It is possible to add more words to make a scientific name more descriptive, for example *Gomphus* (*Phanogomphus*) *cavillaris cavillaris* Needham, 1902. Here *Gomphus* is a genus with many species, (*Phanogomphus*) in parentheses is a Subgenus containing several of those species, the first *cavillaris* is the Species adjective, the second *cavillaris* indicates the first described Subspecies, and Needham is the name of the scientist who first described the subspecies, done in 1902. For most purposes, however, the two-word scientific name is sufficient.

One to several Genera ("jen-ur-ah," the plural of Genus) are grouped together into a Family. North American dragonflies are classified in 7 Families, and all of these are found in the Florida Peninsula. The characteristics of these families are given individually later in this book. The reader will note that the scientific names of the families always end in -idae ("id-dee").

Distribution of Dragonflies in the Florida Peninsula

The state of Florida is L-shaped, with a western Panhandle and an eastern Peninsula. The boundary between these 2 areas for the purposes of this book is the Aucilla River at the eastern edge of Jefferson County. This boundary lies at the narrowest part of the bend of the Florida "L." The Florida Peninsula is larger than most people realize; it stretches approximately 595 km (375 mi) from the Georgia border to the southern tip, and the Keys extend about 155 km (100 mi) southwest from there. The Dry Tortugas Islands lie about 110 km (68 mi) west of Key West.

About 43% of the 86 dragonfly species resident in the Florida Peninsula range over the entire Peninsula, while others are restricted in their range by habitat availability and temperature. From the dragonfly point of view, the Florida Peninsula has 3 major habitat areas. 1) The first is the northern 1/6 of the Peninsula, south to Gainesville. This is the southernmost extent of the more or less continuous part of the eastern deciduous forest, often referred to in Florida as Mesic Hammock Forest. Of the dragonfly species resident in the Florida Peninsula, about 13% do not range further south than Gainesville. 2) The second major habitat area is the middle 1/2 of the Peninsula, between Gainesville and Lake Okeechobee. The latter is the southern extent of the sandy central Florida ridge. It provides the elevation for streams to flow, and forms the basins for clear-water, infertile, sand-bottomed lakes. Thus dragonflies which require a flowing water or sand-bottom lake habitat are seldom found south of Lake Okeechobee. A few species range a little further south, to the latitute of Fort Myers-Palm Beach, or to Naples. Some species have the southern borders of their ranges at approximately the latitude of Ocala, Orlando, or Tampa, and these are probably limited in their distribution by temperature more than by habitat. In all, about 29% of the resident dragonfly species are found little if any further south than Lake Okeechobee. 3) The third major habitat area is the subtropical southern 1/3 of the Peninsula. About 15% of the resident species are seldom found north of Lake Okeechobee, and most of these are not found elsewhere in the U.S. The best places to see these species are vegetated ponds in the Miami area, in spite of the ecological upheavals there. The Keys and the Dry Tortugas Islands do not harbor many dragonfly species, because there is practically no surface fresh water on the islands. The marshes of the Everglades also have a surprisingly limited number of species.

Dragonfly Anatomy

Scientists who read this section may shudder at the use of various terms. However, the aim of this book is to keep things as simple as possible while being scientifically accurate. In the paragraphs below the scientific term for a structure is given in parentheses following the term used in this book.

Some very useful words are those denoting placement of structures relative to each other. *Dorsal* refers to the "back" or the "top" side, whereas *ventral* refers to the "underside" or "bottom." *Anterior* means toward the "front," *posterior* means toward the "rear." *Lateral* refers to the right and left sides. As some examples, the head lies anterior to the thorax, the wings lie dorsal to the legs, spots on the top of the abdomen are dorsal spots, and stripes on the sides of the thorax are lateral stripes.

Stripes are markings which extend along the longitudinal axis of a body part, *Bands* lie perpendicular to the longitudinal axis. Thus, for example, stripes extend lengthwise in a wing, bands are placed across the wing.

The Head:

The most arresting feature of the dragonfly head is its *eye* (compound eye). It is made of many small eyes fused together and forming facets on its surface. A large dragonfly may have 30,000 facets in each eye, looking in all directions except straight to the rear. The eyes of most species are so large that they meet on top of the head. One can tell how good a dragonfly's vision is in various directions by looking at its eyes from different points of view and noting the size of the darkest black spot (pseudopupil). The larger the spot, the more of the eye is looking at you and the better its vision is in that direction. The vision of dragonflies is best forward and upward, not as good to the sides, and poorest to the rear. Other black spots in the eye are internal reflections of the main pseudopupil. Usually the dorsal facets are larger and a darker color than the ventral ones. Larger facets give better vision, and the darker color is probably protection from the sun. In this book, eye color refers to the dorsal eye color unless stated otherwise. The dragonfly eye cannot be focused for different distances, nor can it be quickly adjusted for changing light levels. Yet dragonflies can see each other, at least against the sky, up to about 30 m away, and they can apparently see well while flying through alternate sunlight and shade. Some can see gnats practically in the dark, but no truly nocturnal dragonfly is known. Dragonflies can distinguish the colors we can see, plus ultraviolet, and some species have an ultraviolet color pattern invisible to us. They can also see the degree of polarization of light, and can detect flickering of light at twice the rate that we can. They may use the polarization pattern of light from the sky to navigate, while their ability to see fast moving objects might mean that they could see the pattern on beating wings. In addition to the large compound eyes, dragonflies have 3 small eyes (ocelli) set like jewels in the dorsal anterior part of the head. These are used for sensing the general light level, and to keep track of the horizon during flight.

The other main sense organs on the head are the *antennae*. These are small and bristle-like, probably more useful as wind-speed or flight-speed indicators than as organs of smell. The antennae of larval dragonflies are much larger and help them find prey at night and in murky water where eyes are less useful. So far as known, dragonflies are deaf and do not respond to sounds.

The *Forehead* (dorsal surface of the frons) is often differently colored from the *Face* (labrum, clypeus, and anterior surface of frons) and is used to identify mates and rivals when dragonflies are face to face. The mouthparts contain, from anterior to posterior, an upper lip (labrum), 2 toothy jaws (mandibles) which move from side to side, 2 accessory jaws (maxillae) which also move laterally, and a three-lobed lower lip (labium). Dragonflies usually catch small prey directly in their mouthparts. By lifting the upper lip, dropping the lower lip, and spreading the jaws and accessory jaws to the sides, quite a large funnel-like opening is formed. Larger prey is caught with the bristly legs. When a dragonfly flies out from a perch and returns, an observer cannot often see the tiny insect it was chasing, but the chomping of the jaws indicates when the foray was successful. Dragonflies drink by flopping into the water 3 times, then swallowing a drop of water trapped in the mouthparts. The remarkable thing about this behavior is that they almost always flop 3 times into the water, rarely more or less. The same behavior may be used for cooling and for cleaning; for example females often flop into the water 3 times after egg laying to wash off any remaining eggs.

The Thorax:

The thorax is composed of 3 segments, each bearing a pair of legs. The first segment (prothorax) is small and neck-like, and is not further considered in this book. The second and third segments are fused into a strong box (synthorax) which bears 2 pairs of wings. This box is

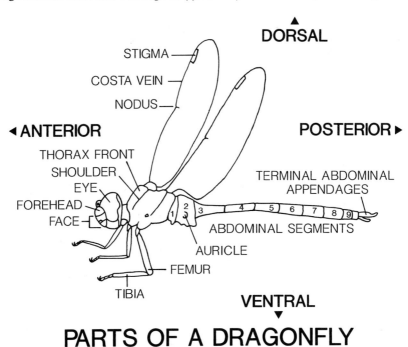

PARTS OF A DRAGONFLY

tipped rearward dorsally, so that the wings are displaced rearward relative to the legs. Thus a dragonfly can perch on the side of a vertical stem with its wings free of interference for a quick takeoff. The anterior sloping surface of the box (mesepisterna) is called the *Front* of the thorax, the "corners" (humeral sutures) at each side of the front are called the *Shoulders*. One of the openings to the respiratory system, which can be closed by an eyelid-like flap, can be seen as a tiny hole on the side of the thorax above the base of the hind leg.

The wings are supported by a network of veins, which are tubes carrying blood, air ducts, and nerves throughout the wing. Thus the veins contain living tissues, but the membranous parts of the wing are mostly non-living cuticle. The veins bear tiny hairs which detect the pattern of air flow over the wings, and relay this information to the computer-like nervous system. The arrangement of the veins is characteristic of each genus or species, and in fact is the major feature by which dragonflies are classified, but little knowledge of wing venation is necessary for the use of this book. The anterior vein of each wing is especially thick, and is called the *Costa*. Near the middle of the wing the costa joins other large veins at a slight notch (nodus). Each wing has a colored spot or *Stigma* (pterostigma) near the tip. It is a blood-filled blister whose weight is thought to reduce wing vibrations interfering with air flow over the wings.

Adult dragonflies hardly walk at all, instead they fly wherever they go. During a takeoff, a dragonfly may beat the fore- and hindwings synchronously for maximum lift, but it soon shifts to alternating the strokes of the forewings and hindwings. That is, while the forewings are flapping upward, the hindwings are usually flapping downward, and vice versa. However, a dragonfly can control the movements of each wing independently, which allows it to do amazing things. It can fly backward for a short distance, but this is not usually necessary because it can spin within its length to fly in the opposite direction within the space of a few wing beats. The wings beat about 50 times per second, producing a low pitched hum which can be heard only when a dragonfly is close to our ears. While a dragonfly can fly very fast for its size, and can dodge faster than the human eye can focus, its actual top speed is not great, about 55 kph (35 mph).

The Abdomen:

The abdomen consists of 10 segments, numbered from 1 at the base to 10 at the tip. Segment 1 is short and inconspicuous, segments 2 and 3 are somewhat inflated, and in males house the accessory genitalia on the underside. Segments 7, 8, and 9 are enlarged in some species to form an abdominal *Club*. Segment 10 bears the *Terminal Abdominal Appendages*; in males 2 dorsal appendages (cerci) and 1 ventral appendage (epiproct), in females just 2 dorsal appendages because the ventral appendage is short and inconspicuous (see Fig. 18). Females may have an *Ovipositor* or egg laying device on the underside of segment 9 (see Figs. 17, 45, and 89).

Sex Differences:

In the Skimmer Family, males and females may have different body colors (see Figs. 71, 72, and 73), or even a different wing pattern (see Figs. 62-63), but in most other dragonflies sex differences are less blatant. The abdomen in females is stouter, more cylindrical, more bluntly tipped, and has larger pale markings, especially on the sides. If the abdomen is clubbed, the club is relatively smaller in females. In females with ovipositors, those can be seen in side view as a bulge, spike, or triangular spout extending from the underside of segment 9. At close range one can see that females have 2 terminal abdominal appendages while males have 3. Except for the Skimmer Family and the Green Darners (genus *Anax*), males have a non-movable lateral flap (auricle) on each side of segment 2, and the base of each hindwing is "cut-out" to clear the flap, forming a "corner" on each hindwing. The flaps of segment 2 are used as guides by females to attain the proper position for mating. In side view, the accessory male genitalia on the underside of segment 2 may be visible, but if not, the lower margin of segment 2 makes a definite angle with segment 3 in males.

Typical Life History of a Dragonfly

The Egg:

All dragonflies lay eggs in or near water, or in a place which will fill with rainwater. The eggs are rod-shaped in the Petaltail and Darner Families, but round or oval in outline, and usual-

6

ly covered with sticky jelly, in the other families. Freshly deposited eggs are usually yellow to orange, but are green in the Cruiser Family and in some Skimmers. The eggs turn darker a few hours after being laid. The eggs of many species hatch in about 10 days, or as little as 5 days in species which breed in temporary pools, or as much as several months for species in which eggs survive the winter or dry conditions.

Dragonfly eggs are eaten by mites, and parasitized by tiny wasps (Fairyflies, family Mymaridae) which can fly underwater to find the eggs. Mold kills many eggs.

The Larva:

Many scientists call immature dragonflies nymphs or naiads, but most now refer to them as larvae. The face of the larva appears gargoyle-like because of the unique lower lip. This is elongated to as much as 1/3 the body length, and has two bristly movable lobes (palps) at the end. When not in use, this lip-trap is folded back under the head and front part of the thorax, but when prey comes within range the trap is shot out in 1/100 second and the victim is clutched between the lobes, then brought back to be chewed by the jaws. In larvae of the Spiketail, Cruiser, Emerald, and Skimmer Families, the lobes of the lip-trap cover most of the face like a mask. Dragonfly larvae capture most kinds of smaller animals that come near, for example worms, aquatic insects such as mosquito larvae, or even snails or smaller dragonfly larvae. Larger dragonfly larvae can catch small fish, but on the other hand dragonfly larvae are a favorite food of many fish, as well as of waterfowl, turtles and other animals.

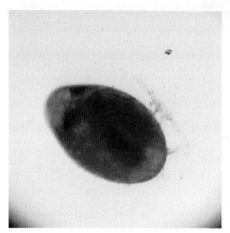

Fig. 3. Egg of Blue Dasher *Pachydiplax longipennis* as seen through a microscope. Developing eyes, jaws, and gills can be seen as dark spots.

A second remarkable feature of dragonfly larvae is that their gills are developed from longitudinal folds of the rectum, and water is breathed in and out of the anus. This arrangement has two advantages. First, the delicate gills are protected internally, and second, water can be shot out the anus with considerable force, giving the larva rapid jet propulsion. It has been found that larvae exhale more forcefully than they inhale. Therefore the "used" water is ejected further from the body, and fresher water is available near the body for the next breath. The anus is surrounded by 5 sharp spines, and dorsal and lateral abdominal spines are also often present. These spines apparently help a larva to escape when it is attacked from the rear.

Dragonfly larvae have various body forms, adapted for different ways of life. Some are flattened and sprawl on the bottom or cling to underwater objects, while others are more cylindrical and either burrow in the bottom or clamber among roots and stems. Some are smooth skinned with a mottled brown or green pattern, others are brown, hairy, and covered with debris.

A larva grows by periodically molting its skin (non-living cuticle of the exoskelton), which happens 8 to 16 times during its life, depending on the species. The life span of a larva varies with species and temperature from a month to several years. In a full grown larva the developing wings are much longer than broad, and extend to about abdominal segment 4. As the time for adult emergence nears, an internal metamorphosis occurs, in which the adult colors may be visible through the larval skin, the large adult eyes can be seen through the skin on top of the head, the developing wings swell, and the lower lip shrinks internally to the adult size. Thus for a few days before transformation to the adult, the larva cannot capture prey and does not eat. In many species the larva moves to the surface of the water and starts to breathe air at this time.

Fig. 4. Larva of Comet Darner *Anax longipes*. Note the lip-trap, exceptionally long in this species, folded under head and thorax.

Fig. 5. Larva of Comet Darner showing internal metamorphosis to the adult. Note adult eyes in contact on top of head, thorax swollen with flight muscles, and swollen wings with accordioned costa vein. Red coloration of adult male abdomen is also visible.

The transformation from larva to adult is definitely something worth watching. The larva usually climbs up on a vertical support at night and hooks its claws firmly into the support. However, Clubtails commonly emerge horizontally on the bank in daylight. The dragonfly swallows air, causing pressure which splits the larval skin first on top of the thorax, then on the head. As the adult continues to swallow air, it rises up out of the larval skin (exuviae) like a pale ghost. The white thread-like linings of the respiratory air tubes are pulled out of the respiratory openings of the thorax. Dragonflies on a vertical support hang by the abdomen with the head downward for about half an hour until the legs are hardened, then they reach up and pull the abdomen out of the larval skin so that they face upward and can use gravity to help lengthen the wings and abdomen. The wings are inflated first, using blood pressure, and at this time have a characteristic sheen given by the thin layer of blood between the upper and lower surfaces. Finally the abdomen is inflated to full length by the continued swallowing of air. Water drips from the tip of the abdomen as it is squeezed out of the rectum by air pressure. Note that the dragonfly must hold its breath until its skin hardens, about 1 1/2 hours for many species. However, it gets oxygen through its moist skin and from the air that it has swallowed. All during emergence, the dragonfly is completely soft and helpless, and if knocked off its perch by the wind, a wave, or a boat wake, it will die. Also many enemies such as blackbirds and ants attack at this time. The wings of a dragonfly during transformation are at first held together over the back, but at the end of emergence the wings are suddenly flicked out to the sides where they will remain for the rest of the dragonfly's life. Soon, often at dawn, the dragonfly takes off on its maiden flight and leaves the vicinity of the water.

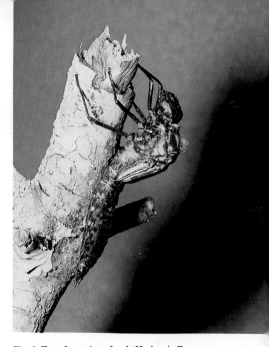

Fig. 6. Transformation of male Harlequin Darner *Gomphaeschna furcillata* at night. Top of adult thorax and eyes are emerging from larval skin as adult swallows air to enlarge its body.

Fig. 7. Adult hangs from larval skin for 29 minutes. Note white thread-like linings of air tubes have been pulled from within adult thorax.

Fig. 8. Adult reaches up to pull abdomen free of larval skin.

Fig. 9. Adult inflates wings using blood pressure and gravity. Inflated male genitalia under abdominal segment 2 can be seen.

The Adult:

    The juvenile adult, over the course of about a week to a month, depending on the species, temperature, and food supply, gradually hardens its skin as it feeds. It may also change color, particularly in males. The pale colors may become brighter or may be obscured and disappear. Especially in males of the Skimmer Family, various parts of the body or wings become covered by a waxy powder or *pruinescence*, like the bloom on plums or grapes. The pruinescence is usually white or pale blue, but in the Slaty Skimmer it is black.

    Dragonflies perch in various ways. Species of the Petaltail, Darner, and Cruiser Families usually perch or hang vertically. Species of the Clubtail Family generally perch horizontally on the ground or a leaf. Most other dragonflies perch obliquely on the sides of stems, but many species of the Skimmer Family perch horizontally on the tips of stems. Some of these, called Pennants, allow the breeze to lift their wings, flag-like. Other Skimmers, called Gliders, do not perch much and feed during sustained flights, gliding periodically on their widened hindwings. Many Skimmers fold their forelegs behind their heads and do not use them to clasp a perch except in windy conditions (see Fig. 85). They may also rest the sides of the hindlegs against a perch, thus actually only holding a perch with the claws of the middle pair of legs. Such perching styles allow for a more unimpeded takeoff. On hot days, some species of dragonflies raise the abdomen nearly straight up. This is called the *obelisk* position (see Fig. 91) and helps prevent overheating by reducing the surface area exposed to the sun. On cool days, dragonflies bask by holding the body perpendicular to the sun. Most species of dragonflies are most active on sunny days and are difficult to find on overcast, cold, or rainy days. In this book meters (m) and centimeters (cm) are used to describe the heights of perches and similar measurements. The reader wishing to use the English system may consider meters equal to yards and a centimeter equal to half an inch.

    At sexual maturity, the male of most species returns to the water and patrols over it searching for females. Males of some species defend a territory against all other males of their species, and sometimes against other species as well. Males of a European species, the Broad-bodied Chaser (*Libellula depressa*), select as a territory that place where they first successfully mated,

10

Fig. 10. Wings fully inflated 16 minutes after facing upward. Note wings are held over back during emergence.
Fig. 11. Abdomen fully lengthened with adult now much longer than larva. Wings show characteristic sheen of a newly emerged dragonfly due to a thin layer of blood still in wings. Adult has held its breath for the nearly 2 hours needed for transformation because the skin was not hard enough to anchor breathing muscles.

and this probably holds true for some American species too. A female looking for a mate or attempting to lay eggs is seized by, usually, the nearest male. He flies above her and grasps her head and thorax with his legs, then curves his abdomen to grasp the top rear part of her head with his terminal abdominal appendages. He then releases his legs, and the pair is now said to be in the *tandem* position. The male curls his abdomen downward and forward, so that sperm from the pore on the underside of abdominal segment 9 can be transferred to the accessory genitalia on the underside of segment 2. He then straightens his abdomen and the female, if ready to mate, bends her abdomen downward and forward to receive the sperm from the male's secondary genitalia. All these events occur in rapid succession and it is difficult to discern the individual steps in the process. The pair is now in the *wheel* position (see Fig. 41), which lasts only a few seconds in some species, more than an hour in others. The male of some species raises his abdomen so that the female's wings are more horizontal which allows her to assist with the flight, but if the wheel position is maintained for more than a few seconds or minutes, depending on the species, the pair usually perches to complete mating. Some, perhaps most, male dragonflies have structures which remove sperm present in the reproductive tract of a female before the male injects his own. In many cases a male dragonfly will hang onto his mate, or at least guard her from other males, so that the eggs she lays will be fertilized by his own most recently deposited sperm.

Female dragonflies lay their eggs or *oviposit* in various ways. In the Petaltail and Darner Families the ovipositor contains 2 pairs of curved knife-like blades within a sheath (see Fig. 28). These blades make holes in a plant stem, soft wood, or soil in which the eggs can be deposited. The sheaths of this type of ovipositor have a pair of tiny feelers (styli) which the female uses to find the exact spot to place each egg. In the Spiketail Family, the sheaths have been reduced, while the blades have become straight and spike-like (see Fig. 45). Female Spiketails use their ovipositors to make holes in the silt of a stream as they hover over shallow water. In some species of the Clubtail, Emerald, and Skimmer Families, the ovipositor is reduced still more, and appears like a triangular spout (see Fig. 89). This type of ovipositor is used like a pick. While the

11

female hovers over an algae mat, mud, or similar soft substrate, downward swings of the abdomen cause the ovipositor to make little pits in which the eggs rest. In other dragonflies the ovipositor is so reduced that it is said to be lacking. All that remains is 1 pair of blades (now called the subgenital plate) which appear flap-like or lobe-like (the styli also remain). Females without an ovipositor usually tap the water with the abdomen to wash off eggs, but a few species drop the eggs while in flight or perched.

In the Common Green Darner and some species of the Skimmer Family, the male retains his hold on the female's head after mating, and the pair oviposits in the tandem position (see Fig. 14). In other species, the male releases the female but guards her by hovering or perching over her and driving away other males while she oviposits. In still other species mated females attempt to sneak back to the water at a place or time when they can lay their eggs without interference from males. One mating provides enough sperm to fertilize several batches of eggs of several hundred each.

The main enemies of mature dragonflies are frogs, certain birds such as flycatchers and kites, and larger dragonflies. Spiders and robber flies also capture many dragonflies. Two types of external parasites attack dragonflies. The most common are green or red mites which crawl from the larva to the soft adult when a dragonfly transforms (see Fig. 104). The mites usually sink their mouthparts in the underside of the dragonfly's thorax or abdomen. These mites are found almost exclusively on pond dwelling dragonflies of the Skimmer Family, and they eventually drop off a dragonfly into the water to complete their life cycle. A second type of parasite is a biting gnat (Family Ceratopogonidae) which sucks the blood from a wing vein even while the dragonfly is in flight. This gnat (*Forcipomyia fusicornis*) is most common near the coasts, and is a specialist parasite of dragonflies and damselflies.

Photographing Dragonflies

Most of the photographs in this book were made with a 35 mm single lens reflex (SLR) camera with a 55 mm macro lens and ASA 64 film. This type of camera permits the photographer to look through the same lens that the photo will be taken through, thus "what you see is (more or less!) what you get." Also, a built-in light meter gauges the light through the same lens. The macro lens permits close-ups, but to fill the picture with a medium sized dragonfly using a 55 mm lens requires that the film be only about 30 cm (12 in) from the dragonfly, and the end of the lens is only about 15 cm from the insect. Many dragonflies will not allow such a close approach, so a 100 mm macro lens would be better because it allows the same size image from twice the distance. A 200 mm macro lens is also good except that a tripod must always be used. A tripod is necessary to obtain the sharpest photos with any size lens, but is rather inconvenient and time consuming to set up. I do not use a tripod for most dragonfly photography, but that results in throwing away a lot of photos. An electronic flash solves the problem of camera shake, but does not look as natural as sunlight. If the background is far away, it will not be lit by the flash and will appear black. I find it easiest to pre-set the focus for the size image I want, then approach the dragonfly with the camera at my eye until it is in sharp focus, then press the shutter. Any subsequent adjustments or advancing the film are made with slow smooth movements.

As film speed or sensitivity to light increases, from ASA 25 to ASA 400 for example, the film gets grainier, resulting in fuzzier images. I find ASA 64 a good compromise between speed and graininess, because an in-focus photo on this film can be greatly enlarged and still appear sharp. Using ASA 64 film in full sunlight, I use a shutter opening of about f8 at 1/60 second, or f5.6 at 1/125 second. The most difficult thing in dragonfly photography is to get both the head and the tip of the abdomen in focus at the same time. It is very difficult to get everything right for a photo of a wild dragonfly, thus most of the photos in this book were posed, using live but stunned or cooled dragonflies. Sometimes a dragonfly is stunned by the net during capture and will allow a photo or two before it flies away. Dragonflies can be cooled in a refrigerator or ice chest and a couple of photos can be taken, perhaps, before they warm up and fly away. You will find that photographing even stunned dragonflies is not easy, and the most essential ingredient is patience. It is quite astounding how much can go wrong in the instant it takes to press a shutter release!

Collecting Dragonflies

Collecting of insects in moderation does no harm, and in fact does a great deal of good if the specimens are well preserved, well labelled, and given to an interested museum when the collector is finished with them or dies. Almost all the information in this book came from collectors, and collectors will continue to be an important source of data on dragonflies in the forseeable future. I typically collect 1 or 2 specimens of each species at each different habitat I visit. By far the most important part of collecting is writing down WHERE and WHEN each specimen was taken ON THE SAME DAY it was collected. Specimens without these data are worthless, or less than worthless if the data are wrong due to a faulty memory. Useful data are the state, county, nearest town, nearest water body, nearest highway, date, time of day, weather, name of the collector, habitat notes, and behavior notes. Specimens of particular scientific interest are associated pairs labelled as In Tandem or In Wheel, and adults associated with the larval skin from which they emerged. In the latter case, let the adult harden for a day in a brown paper bag before preservation.

The best dragonfly net is as large, strong, and light in weight as possible. I use a modified fish landing net with a hoop about 50 cm (1 1/2 ft) in diameter, a handle 2 m (6 ft) long, and a net bag with meshes a few mm across for low air resistance. A dark net bag is probably better than a white one, and it must be tough to resist thorns. Dragonflies are best approached slowly, then the net is swung as fast as possible from the rear of the insect. The net swing should be followed through until the dragonfly is deep in the bag, then the handle is rotated to close the entrance to the net. You will have plenty of chances to admire dragonflies' skill at evading a net! To remove a dragonfly from the net, hold the wings together above its back and keep the jaws from clamping on the net. A dragonfly will often hold the net with its jaws until the head is pulled off. Place the insect in an envelope with its wings over its back and abdomen straight. If it can curl its abdomen to its mouth, it will chew off the end of its own abdomen. Place the envelope in a crush-proof container and protect it from excessive heat until you get home. Use of a killing bottle is not desirable, because dragonflies begin to lose their colors soon after death.

Dragonflies can be killed in a few seconds by dropping them in a wide-mouthed bottle of acetone. They can also be put to sleep in a freezer, but the blue or green colors of some species will darken, and decomposition is rapid once they are thawed. After death, arrange each specimen with wings over its back and abdomen straight in a paper envelope, and place the whole envelope in a jar of acetone. Acetone draws the water out of the specimens, thus drying them, and it kills bacteria which cause decomposition, as well as dissolving some of the body fats. Acetone can be bought in paint or hardware stores, but note that it is as FLAMMABLE as gasoline, and its fumes should not be breathed. Write data on a flap of the envelope with a pencil, because acetone will dissolve some kinds of inks. The acetone is reuseable, but when it becomes yellow from dissolved fats, throw it on a driveway and let it evaporate, and replace with fresh acetone. After soaking the specimens in acetone for about 24 hours, remove the envelopes and dry them in a stream of air from an air conditioner or from a hair dryer set at a distance of about 1 m on the lowest heat. The specimens are dry in about 1 to 2 hours when the legs and abdomen do not move with gentle finger pressure. This acetone treatment preserves the pattern and most of the colors, but some fading will occur. There is no known way to preserve eye colors, so you may wish to take notes on coloration before preserving the specimen.

Specimens can be stored in paper or glassine envelopes such as those used by stamp collectors. Even better are transparent plastic envelopes containing a 3 X 5 inch data card along with the specimen, but such envelopes are not currently being manufactured in the U.S. The envelopes can be stored on edge like cards in a card file in plastic shoe boxes or other tight containers, with a few naphthalene moth balls in each box to repel beetles and other pests (paradichlorobenzene moth balls will dissolve some kinds of plastic). At all times the specimens must be protected from beetles, booklice, roaches, ants, mice, and from high humidity which will allow mold to grow. Pinning is not a good method for preserving dragonflies because the head and abdomen break off so easily.

When you are finished with your collection, or if you find a specimen that seems of particular importance, the International Odonata Research Institute would like to receive donations or have the opportunity to examine such specimens. It is a good idea to state the final disposition for your collection in your will. The current address for the International Odonata Research Institute is:

International Odonata Research Institute
P. O. Box 1269
Gainesville, FL 32602-1269

If you are interested in joining the international dragonfly society (Societas Internationalis Odonatologica), write to the same address. Members each year receive 4 issues of the top-quality journal Odonatologica, 2 issues of the smaller journal Notulae Odonatologicae, and 2 issues of the newsletter Selysia, plus book catalogues and meeting announcements. The society holds an international symposium every other year, and a meeting in the U.S. almost every year. The society is currently headquartered in The Netherlands, and dues fluctuate with the value of the guilder (Hfl) relative to the U.S. dollar. Annual dues are currently about $60 U.S.

To mail specimens, place the envelopes containing them in a small box with padding to prevent the envelopes from shifting, because if the envelopes can slide back and forth the specimens will be shattered. Then place the small box with padding around it in a larger box. Label the latter "Fragile," and "Contents: Dead Insects, No Commercial Value."

Dragonflies in Education

Adult dragonflies are not laboratory animals, but they do offer exciting subjects for field study. The best place would be a clean pond with emergent vegetation along the edges but clear banks. The aquatic vegetation offers perches for the dragonflies, and the clear bank allows students comfort and ease of movement. Students can spread out along the bank and each can watch an individual male dragonfly on his territory. Observations on ecology and behavior are noted and can be quantified if desired. A recording chart can be provided by the instructor on which students can record the number of times particular acts are performed, such as prey capture, aggressive chases within the same species, aggression between species, and territorial displays. The student may also pay special attention to the orientation of perching dragonflies with respect to the perch itself, wind direction, sun, open water surface, and neighboring dragonflies. If a female dragonfly arrives in the student's vicinity, courtship display, mating, oviposition, and guarding of the female may be seen. As a term project, students could net and mark individuals with coded dots of paint on abdomen or wings, and record dragonfly activity over a longer time. Thus information on life span, fidelity to a territory, local movements, reproductive potential, and population size can be obtained.

For another type of outdoor laboratory, numerous behavior experiments can be done. For instance, models made from colored pieces of wood with plastic wings can be presented to male dragonflies. Presentation is done by dangling the model from a thread on the end of a pole, or it can be pinned to a perch. The size, color, motion, and other features of the model can be altered to find out which characteristics release the insect's instinctive behaviors. For some experiments along these lines, see Andrew (1966), Jacobs (1955), and Johnson (1962).

In the classroom, eggs and larvae offer interesting learning. Eggs are most easily obtained from a female Skimmer caught while ovipositing. If she is held by the hind wings and her abdomen dipped to the surface of water in a jar, she will probably release hundreds of eggs. To keep them alive, use aged or dechlorinated tap water which is better than pond water because the eggs are less likely to mold. Eggs can be placed under the microscope to observe day to day embryological development, and with luck, the hatching process (this often occurs early in the morning). Larvae are very interesting to watch catching and eating their prey, and experiments can be conducted on the amount of food required for maximum growth rate, and on the interactions between equal-sized larvae (careful, small larvae will merely be food for bigger ones!). Transformation to the adult is absolutely fascinating and can be predicted as described in the life history section above.

Dragonfly Conservation

A few human activities benefit some dragonflies, such as pond building. Newly created ponds benefit certain species that can not compete well with species of long-established ponds. On the other hand, people typically introduce fish into ponds, which greatly reduces dragonfly populations, and eliminates some species.

Stream dragonflies have been much more severely impacted by human activities than pond species. Pesticides kill dragonfly larvae, and sewage and organic wastes from industries such as paper mills cause bacterial growth which reduces the oxygen content of the water. Fertilizer run-off from orchards and lawns causes algae to grow which also use excessive oxygen at night. Silt from eroding land changes bottom characteristics and blocks the light needed by eelgrass and other plants. Siltation and even destruction of the streambed is especially severe where livestock are allowed to graze the banks, forest is clear cut to the banks, or fields are plowed to the banks. Dredging, ditching, and channelization pretty much destroy a stream biologically. A buffer zone of forest 20-30 m or so wide on each side of a stream will help prevent erosion. After all, a farmer or forester does want the soil to remain on the land, not in the water. General deforestation of the watershed of a stream leads to reduced water holding capacity of the land, resulting in alternating floods which wash away dragonfly larvae, and droughts which reduce the area in which they live. Thus a good population of stream-dwelling dragonflies, particularly Clubtails which generally have a 2 year life cycle, is an indicator of a healthy environment and good water quality. Because of the low relief, damming of streams is not a great problem in the Florida Peninsula. But in other areas rare stream dragonflies are being replaced by common pond species. The worst habitats are reservoirs with fluctuating water levels which prevent aquatic plants from growing at the edges. There, few dragonflies, even pond species, can survive. Clean streams are rapidly becoming rarer, because somewhere along the stream, someone is likely to lower water quality by doing one of the things mentioned above. Note that the larger a stream, the greater the cumulative effect of the above influences. Therefore a clean large river, such as the Suwannee, is a treasure to be protected at all costs.

Special dragonfly habitats, such as forest seeps or sphagnum bogs should be protected from lumbering, grazing, or development. Fortunately, a sanctuary of just a few acres may be enough to protect a population of rare dragonflies and associated plants and animals. No such sanctuaries for dragonflies have been established in the U.S., although such have been developed in Japan.

Of special concern to Florida residents should be the protection of sand-bottomed lakes. These are the habitat of 3 species and 1 subspecies of dragonfly which are not found outside of Florida, as well as other unusual dragonflies. Residents in developments around these lakes should not establish lawns, or if they do, they should not use fertilizers and pesticides on their lawns. As fertilizer runs into the lake, the water changes from clear to green due to algae growth, and the bottom changes from sand to muck as the algae die and decompose. This is the process of eutrophication, and it will reduce property values on the shore of lakes where it occurs. For the same reasons, sewage should be piped far from such lakes for processing, and septic tanks should not be used near these lakes. A wide buffer zone of weeds around lakes in citrus groves would help protect those waters from fertilizer runoff and pesticide drift.

Dunkle and Westfall (1982) discussed dragonfly conservation in Florida. Bick (1983), Carle (1979), and Shiffer (1985) discussed dragonfly conservation there and elsewhere in the U.S.

DRAGONFLIES
OF THE
FLORIDA PENINSULA

Fig. 12. Gray Petaltail, male.

PETALTAILS
Family Petaluridae

These large insects are the "dinosaurs" among dragonflies. In Mesozoic times they were a dominant group, as the dinosaurs were then. Now only 9 species of Petaltails survive at scattered spots around the globe. This family is distinguished by a combination of characteristics. The eyes are widely spaced as in the Clubtail Family, but the female has an ovipositor with blades as in the Darner Family. Males of some foreign species have large petal-like terminal abdominal appendages. In North America, 1 species occurs throughout the eastern U.S., 1 other species, the Black Petaltail (*Tanypteryx hageni*), is found in the Pacific Northwest.

GRAY PETALTAIL
Genus *Tachopteryx*

This genus includes only the large gray and black dragonfly species described below.

GRAY PETALTAIL   *Tachopteryx thoreyi*

Identification: Northern Florida, uncommon and local, size large, 71-83 mm (2.8-3.3 in) long.

This is our only large gray and black dragonfly, and our only large one which habitually perches on tree trunks. The eyes are widely spaced, but the female has an ovipositor with blades. The stigma is distinctively long, narrow, and ribbon-like.

Ecology: Found south to Gainesville. Ranges north to New Hampshire, southernmost Quebec, and Michigan, west to central Oklahoma and eastern Texas. The flight season is in the spring, recorded from March 8 to June 19 in Florida. The flat, leaf-like larvae live among wet leaves either above or below the water surface in permanent hillside seepages in hardwood hammock forest.

Behavior: The Gray Petaltail usually perches on sunny tree trunks, but may occasionally perch on the ground or on weed stems. Usually not wary, it will also perch on a motionless person. It attacks both small and large insects, including large butterflies, large moths, and other dragonflies. Males waiting near seepages for females will perch in a sunny spot on almost anything available. They also search for females by flying up and down one tree trunk after another. Mating occurs in the forest canopy. Females oviposit in wet leaves or mud in seepage areas.

Dunkle (1981) studied the ecology and behavior of this species at Gainesville.

DARNERS
Family Aeshnidae

The Darners are long- and slender-bodied, like a darning needle, and they include the largest Florida Dragonflies. Their eyes are very large and meet in a seam on top of the head. In most species scars can be seen on the eyes of a female where a male has held her during mating (see Dunkle 1979). Females have an ovipositor with blades, as in the Petaltails. Darners hang vertically on a perch whether it is a vertical stem or horizontal twig.

GREEN DARNERS
Genus *Anax*

These large dragonflies have an unmarked bright green thorax. Males differ from other Darners in that they lack flaps or auricles on abdominal segment 2, and the base of the hindwing is rounded as in females. Of the 4 North American species, 3 occur in Florida, though one is a vagrant. The fourth species, the Giant Green Darner (*Anax walsinghami*), is found in the western U.S.

COMMON GREEN DARNER — *Anax junius*

Identification: Common, size large, 68-84 mm (2.7-3.3 in) long.

This species has a black spot on the forehead enclosed by a blue semicircle and forming a distinctive "bulls-eye." Males (rarely females) are easily recognized by their all green thorax and mostly bright blue abdomen. At cool temperatures, the blue darkens to purple. Males have the top of abdominal segment 2 blue, whereas this area is brown in females. Females have gray-green sides on the abdomen. Juveniles of both sexes have a reddish brown to reddish violet abdomen.

Ecology: This is the most widespread and common large dragonfly in North America. It breeds in nearly any still or slowly moving vegetated waters, including temporary or slightly brackish habitats. It is found throughout Florida including the Keys and Dry Tortugas. It ranges throughout the U.S., north into Alaska and the Canadian border provinces, and south into Mexico. The species is also recorded from Hawaii, Tahiti, the east coast of Asia, Bahamas, Bermuda, and the West Indies southeast to Martinique. It can be seen all year in southern Florida, but is most common in spring and fall because it migrates northward during the summer.

Behavior: Unlike most Darners, the Common Green Darner often perches low among weeds and grass. Its prey includes a large variety of insects such as wasps, moths, butterflies, beetles, flies, and medium-sized dragonflies. Two attacks on hummingbirds have been recorded! This species is active from early morning to dark. Between bursts of flapping flight, they sail with the hindwings flat and forewings slightly raised. As mentioned above, it is one of the few migratory dragonflies in North America. Males sporadically patrol irregular territories at a height of about 1 m. They can see each other at a distance of at least 20 m. Mating pairs hang in tall weeds, bushes, or trees. While females may lay eggs alone, this is our only Darner which oviposits while the male holds the female in tandem. The female usually probes beneath the water with her abdomen to place eggs in submerged or floating plants. Occasionally she backs down a stem until completely submerged, a behavior rare among dragonflies. Females also sometimes oviposit in dry algae or mud above water level.

Young (1967) gives more data on this species.

Fig. 13. Common Green Darner, mature male.

Fig. 14. Common Green Darners, ovipositing in tandem. Note the pale ventral terminal abdominal appendage of the male pressed into the eyes of the female.

Fig. 15. Comet Darner, mature male.

Fig. 16. Comet Darner, mature female.

COMET DARNER

Anax longipes

Identification: Uncommon, size large, 75-87 mm (3.0-3.4 in) long.

The unmistakable male is the only North American dragonfly with a green thorax and a fiery red abdomen (pale orange in juveniles). Unlike our other Green Darners, the Comet has an unmarked green forehead. In females the abdomen is green at the base and red- brown beyond, with dull green to tan spots (spots pale blue in juvenile females). In juveniles the eyes are gray, becoming green in males, and blue in females. The legs are very long.

Ecology: The Comet Darner ranges throughout the Florida Peninsula, north to Massachusetts, southern Ontario, and Wisconsin, west into Kansas and Texas. Its habitat consists of borrow pits and semi- permanent, usually grassy, ponds. Apparently its larvae do not compete well with other dragonflies or with fish. The recorded Florida flight season is February 23 to November 23.

Behavior: This species feeds as it flies far and wide on insects up to the size of medium-sized dragonflies. Males are striking—Klots exclaimed (in Needham and Westfall, 1955, p. 272) "Heavenly Day, isn't he a beautiful thing on the wing! With that emerald green of the thorax and blood red of the abdomen, and that striking flash of white from the base of the abdomen." Males patrol 1-2 m above the water in beats up to 50 m long, from about 9 A.M. to late afternoon. Mating occurs while the pair hangs in a tree, and females oviposit in submerged plant stems or algae.

Fig. 17. Ringed Darner, mature female.

RINGED DARNER

Anax amazili

Identification: Rare vagrant, size large.

This species is similar to the Common Green Darner, but the blue semicircle of the bulls-eye mark on the forehead is broken into a blue spot on each side. In side view the mostly brown abdomen looks broadly ringed because segments 3-6 have large basal spots. These spots are dull blue in juveniles but become green at maturity. The eyes are bluish gray.

The Common Green Darner appears to have a striped rather than a ringed abdomen, and the male abdomen is bright blue, including the sides of segment 2 (sides of 2 green in male Ringed).

Ecology: The Ringed Darner is vagrant to Florida, including the Dry Tortugas, and is most likely to be found in southern Florida. It is also vagrant to Texas. The species ranges from Mexico and the West Indies south to Argentina. In the tropics it breeds in weedy ponds, lakes, and ditches, including brackish waters. It probably flies all year in the tropics, but has been recorded in Florida only in July.

Behavior: This species feeds until dark, and is very quick on the wing. Males patrol about 2 m above shoreline vegetation. Females usually oviposit in submerged vegetation, but have been seen laying eggs in grass blades 10 cm above the water.

PILOT DARNERS
Genus *Coryphaeschna*

These are large Darners with long abdomens but short legs. The thorax is mostly green with brown stripes, the abdomen in our species is mostly black with narrow green rings. The forehead has a black T-shaped spot. The females show an interesting reversal of wing coloration; in juveniles the wings are brown-orange at the base and transparent beyond, at maturity they become transparent at the base and brown-orange beyond. The eyes of juveniles and males are green, but they become blue in mature females. Juvenile females of the Florida species have

Fig. 18. Regal Darner, juvenile female.

long ribbon-like terminal abdominal appendages, but these break off in mature females. Three of the four North American species occur in Florida. The Fourth, the Malachite Darner (*Coryphaeschna luteipennis*), is found in Arizona.

The Phantom Darner is similar but its abdomen has a narrow waist at segment 3 in dorsal view. Also the mature male has blue spots dorsally between the wings and at the base of the abdomen.

REGAL DARNER   *Coryphaeschna ingens*

Identification: Common, size very large, 82-100 mm (3.2-4.0 in) long.

One of the largest North American dragonflies. The thorax is green with wide brown stripes, the abdomen is brown with narrow green cross-lines. The eyes are green in juveniles and males, becoming pure blue in mature females. Some females become thinly pruinose and appear pale blue at a distance.

The equally large Swamp Darner has a brown thorax with green stripes, and blue eyes in both sexes.

Ecology: Common throughout the Florida Peninsula, including the Keys and Dry Tortugas. Ranges in the coastal states from central Texas to Virginia, also in Cuba and the Bahamas. Its habitat is densely vegetated lakes and slow streams. The recorded Florida flight season is February 6 to October 19. It is most common in spring, but apparently a few emerge in the fall.

Behavior: Juveniles sail languidly about in clearings, occasionally hanging from twigs or weed stems, but with maturity they fly for long periods at treetop height. Feeding swarms of males are often seen, especially at dusk. The Regal Darner is one of our few dragonflies which does not defend a territory of any kind, and males do not patrol the water. Females land on grass or other plant stems, then quickly back down until abdominal segment 8 is submerged to oviposit in stems just below water level. A female flies from one oviposition site to another with the end of the abdomen curled downward which signals to the males that she is not ready to mate at that time.

25

Fig. 19. Mangrove Darner, male.

MANGROVE DARNER

Coryphaeschna viriditas

Identification: Southern Florida, rare, size very large.

This species is similar to the Regal Darner except that the thorax has very narrow brown lines instead of wide brown stripes.

Ecology: This species has been found in Florida at the southeastern tip of the Peninsula and in the Keys. It ranges elsewhere from northern Mexico to Paraguay, and in the Greater Antilles. It is associated with Mangrove swamps, or ponds and ditches near such swamps. The recorded Florida flight season is March 19 to August 10, but is perhaps all year as in the tropics.

Behavior: So far as known, like the Regal Darner.

Fig. 20. Blue-faced Darner, male. This specimen from Honduras has a paler green thorax than Florida specimens.

BLUE-FACED DARNER   *Coryphaeschna adnexa*

Identification: Southern Florida, scarce, size large, 62-75 mm (2.4- 3.0 in) long.

This species is smaller than our other Pilot Darners, with a darker green thorax which has very narrow brown stripes. Mature males have a sky blue face and blue ventrally in the eyes. Females develop blue eyes at maturity as in our other Pilot Darners. The rear of the head is pale blue in both sexes.

Ecology: This species was first discovered in southeastern Florida in 1980. It ranges south through the Greater Antilles, and from northern Mexico to Argentina. Its habitat is weedy lakes, canals, and marshes. It flies all year in the tropics.

Behavior: This Darner feeds in large irregular beats 1-2 m up over lawns and in clearings. Males may perch with abdominal segments 8-10 angled dorsally. They patrol a short beat 1-2 m up, especially over channels in marsh vegetation. Females oviposit in submerged stems.

Fig. 21. Twilight Darner, mature female. The terminal abdominal appendages are partly broken off, as is usual in mature females of this species. The Cuban Darner *Gynacantha ereagris* of the Bahamas is very similar but has a narrow abdominal waist in females.

TWO-SPINED DARNERS
Genus *Gynacantha*

Only one species of this tropical group of insects occurs in North America. Females have 2 spines on the underside of abdominal segment 10 which are used during egg deposition. Two-spined Darners are mostly large slender dull green or brown dragonflies that are active at dusk and dawn.

TWILIGHT DARNER
Gynacantha nervosa

Identification: Common, size large, 71-80 mm (2.8-3.2 in) long.

This is a slender, plain brown and dull green dragonfly. The female has 2 spines on the underside of abdominal segment 10 which form a fulcrum when she uses her ovipositor blades to lay eggs in soil. The eyes are exceptionally large, brown in juveniles, green at maturity with a horizontal blue bar across the middle. The wings develop a brown tint, first along the front border, becoming all dark brown in aged individuals. The female terminal abdominal appendages are as long as abdominal segments 9 + 10, but become broken off to about half that length.

Some other dragonflies are similar but smaller. The Phantom Darner has a striped thorax. The Fawn Darner has 2 lateral yellow thoracic spots. The Mocha Emerald is darker brown with red-brown or brilliant green eyes.

Ecology: The Twilight Darner occurs throughout peninsular Florida and the Keys, north into Georgia. It has also been found in Texas and Oklahoma, and south to Bolivia, as well as in the Bahamas and West Indies. It flies all year in Florida, but is most abundant in October. This species often survives frost in its dense forest habitat. It breeds in shady temporary pools with emergent plants but without fish.

Behavior: Individuals of this species are usually seen feeding in the open during the last half hour before nightfall, but in cool weather they hunt in forest undergrowth during the day. They often feed in a small area a few m in diameter while prey lasts. Williamson in 1923 (p. 41) wrote:

28

"Where the species occurs abundantly the numbers on the wing and in sight all at once, the mobile active flight, and the rapidly coming darkness of the tropical night combine to form a scene to fire the imagination...three or four are seen circling about a thatched hut and at once the garden and path are alive with interweaving forms and the flight is on. They come from everywhere, the air is filled with them, some fly erratically, others patrol regular beats,.... As suddenly as they appeared, only a few are seen, and then they are gone, and the disappointed collector with possibly only two or three specimens in his bottle, realizes that the twenty to thirty minute flight is at its end, and that he will not see *nervosa* again for twenty-four hours." I have also experienced such swarms, and it is a magical experience to be surrounded by rustling wings in the dusk, insulated from the attacks of mosquitoes by squadrons of personal "fighter escorts." These dragonflies hang in shady retreats during most of the day, such as under cabbage palm leaves or occasionally in buildings. Mating occurs while the pair hangs from a twig in the forest undergrowth. Females warily oviposit during the afternoon or evening in the soil near the edge of pools, or in depressions which will fill with rainwater.

Williams (1937) further described the natural history of this species.

THREE-SPINED DARNERS
Genus *Triacanthagyna*

Only one species of this mostly South American group occurs in North America. Females have 3 spines on the underside of abdominal segment 10 which are used in egg laying. Three-spined Darners are very similar to the Two-spined Darners but are typically smaller and greener, although they have similar crepuscular habits.

Fig. 22. Phantom Darner, mature male.

PHANTOM DARNER

Triacanthagyna trifida

Identification: Common, size fairly large, 62-70 mm (2.4-2.7 in) long.

The thorax of this dragonfly is grass green with brown stripes, the abdomen is brown with small green spots. Juveniles have green eyes, which become deep blue in males, brown in old females. Mature males have sky blue spots between the wings and on the sides of abdominal segments 2 and 3. The female's long ribbon-like terminal abdominal appendages eventually break off. In old females the wings become dark brown. Females have 3 spines on the underside of abdominal segment 10 used as a fulcrum when ovipositing in soil.

Among somewhat similar Darners, the Twilight Darner has an unstriped thorax, the Regal, Mangrove, and Swamp Darners are much larger, and the Blue-faced Darner has only narrow brown lines instead of wide stripes on the front of the thorax.

Ecology: The Phantom Darner breeds in temporary forest pools throughout the Florida Peninsula, as well as in the Keys and Dry Tortugas. It also occurs north to North Carolina, and in the Bahamas and Greater Antilles. The recorded flight season in Florida is July 10 through the winter to January 8. This species can survive several frosts in its dense forest habitat, and is more abundant in wet years. Mature males with blue markings usually appear in October.

Behavior: This is a mostly crepuscular species, flitting about phantom-like in the last 2 hours before nightfall. Like the Twilight Darner they will hold to a beat a few m in diameter until the supply of prey is exhausted. Singles and mating pairs are found hanging from twigs in forest during most of the day. Mature males patrol swiftly in about a 3 m diameter area over muddy depressions which will fill later with rain water, and females oviposit in the soil in such areas.

SWAMP DARNER
Genus *Epiaeschna*

The only species classified in this genus is described below.

30

Fig. 23. Swamp Darner, male.

SWAMP DARNER   *Epiaeschna heros*

Identification: Common, size very large, 77-94 mm (3.0-3.7 in) long.

This species is one of the largest dragonflies in North America. It is dark brown with blue eyes, green stripes on the thorax, and narrow green abdominal rings. The female terminal abdominal appendages are elongate-oval and leaf-like.

The Regal and Mangrove Darners are equally large, but their thorax is green with brown stripes, and only mature females have blue eyes. When flying overhead the wings of juvenile Swamp Darners are tinted yellow in the middle 3/5, but are clear at the base and tip. In Pilot Darners the wings are all clear or are tinted orange-brown either in the basal 1/6 or outer 5/6. The Cyrano Darner is smaller with the abdomen striped lengthwise.

Ecology: The Swamp Darner is common in Florida south to near Lake Okeechobee. It ranges north to Maine, southern Quebec, southern Ontario, and Wisconsin, west to Kansas and eastern Texas. It flies from February 27 to November 1, but is most commonly seen in spring and early summer. Its habitat is shady woodland ponds and slow streams, particularly swampy areas, and includes temporary ponds.

Behavior: This species feeds widely over the countryside from about 1 m above ground to the treetops. The Swamp Darner usually perches by hanging from shady tree branches, but it some-

31

times enters buildings seeking a shady perch. It preys on insects up to the size of cicadas, carpenter bees, and King Skimmer dragonflies. It commonly feeds in swarms, especially at dusk, and swarms containing both sexes quickly gather to attack winged termites or ants. Like the Regal Darner, male Swamp Darners do not hold territories or patrol over water. Mating pairs hang in the trees, and the female later oviposits in mud, wet logs, small tree trunks, or stems from water level up to 2 m above it. She may lay eggs in a dry pond which will later fill with rainwater.

CYRANO DARNER
Genus *Nasiaeschna*

The rather strange dragonfly described below is the only species classified in this genus.

CYRANO DARNER   *Nasiaeschna pentacantha*

Identification: Common, size large, 62-73 mm (2.4-2.9 in) long.

The greenish blue forehead projects forward, nose-like (reminiscent of the nose of the literary character Cyrano de Bergerac). This Darner is dark brown, with dark blue eyes, green thoracic stripes, and 3 interrupted blue-green abdominal stripes (a median stripe, plus a lateral stripe on each side). The abdomen tapers from base to tip in males, but is cylindrical and stout in females. In both sexes the terminal abdominal appendages are barely longer than abdominal segment 10.

Ecology: This species ranges throughout the Florida Peninsula, and north to New Hamphire, southern Quebec, southern Ontario, and Wisconsin, west into Iowa, Kansas, and Texas. It flies from March 2 to November 19. The habitat is swampy streams, lake coves, and ponds with roots and branches in the water.

Behavior: The Cyrano Darner stays in or close to forest, where it hunts prey such as damselflies and King Skimmer dragonflies. Males have a very distinctive patrolling flight about 2 m above the water, so that though they are often dull colored and appear gray at a distance, they can be recognized by their tapered abdomens and flight style. They fly slowly to and fro without hovering and angle the wings upward while vibrating them continuously. The patrols are about 5-30 m long, usually in the morning and in sunlight. The flight appears lazy but they are very quick to drive away all other dragonflies except females of their own species. Females oviposit in wet wood above or below the waterline, or sometimes in wet dead leaves or in water lily leaves.

Fig. 24. Cyrano Darner, male.

Fig. 25. Harlequin Darner, male.

PYGMY DARNERS
Genus *Gomphaeschna*

The 2 species in this genus are the smallest Darners in North America. The male ventral terminal abdominal appendage is deeply forked, unlike that of other North American Darners. Females have short terminal abdominal appendages, about as long as abdominal segment 10.

HARLEQUIN DARNER   *Gomphaeschna furcillata*

Identification: Northern Florida, uncommon, size medium, 48-60 mm (1.9-2.4 in) long.

This is a small, mostly black Darner. The males have bright green eyes (gray in juveniles), and a cylindrical abdomen with green spots on the posterior segments. Females have white lateral spots on the middle abdominal segments and rusty orange dorsal spots on segments 2 to 6. Females usually have an orange tint in the outer half of the forewing.

The Taper-tailed Darner is very similar but more dully colored. Males have a tapered abdomen, eyes with only a green sheen, and only obscure green posterior abdominal spots. Females have rusty orange lateral spots on the middle abdominal segments and dorsal spots on segments 2 and 3. Females sometimes have an orange cloud at the middle of the forewing.

34

Fig. 26. Harlequin Darner, female.

Ecology: This Darner occurs south to Orlando, but ranges north to Nova Scotia, and west in the U.S. to Michigan, Arkansas, and eastern Texas. It breeds in Sphagnum bogs, Bald Cypress swamps, and Alder swamps. This early spring species is recorded in Florida from January 8 to April 22.

Behavior: The Harlequin Darner feeds along forest edges, where they usually perch on tree trunks, or rarely on the ground, both unusual perch sites for a Darner. Their prey includes house flies and winged termites. This is one of the few dragonflies seen more easily on windy days, when swarms, mostly of males, gather to feed in the lee of trees and bushes. Males patrol small areas in bogs or swamps, hovering for long periods but turning to face another direction every few seconds. Sometimes they patrol over land rather than water, for reasons unknown. Females oviposit in wet wood about 15 cm above water level.

Fig. 27. Taper-tailed Darner, male.

TAPER-TAILED DARNER   *Gomphaeschna antilope*

Identification: Rare. See Identification of the very similar Harlequin Darner.

Ecology: The Taper-tailed Darner ranges south to Naples, north to New Jersey and Ohio, and west to Louisiana. It flies a little later in the spring than the Harlequin Darner, and is recorded January 31 to June 9 in Florida. Like the Harlequin, it inhabits swamps and bogs.

Behavior: The behavior is not well known, but appears generally similar to that of the Harlequin Darner. The Taper-tailed perches on tree trunks and hangs under small tree branches. Swarms of males feed in the lee of trees on windy days, and they can see each other at a distance of at least 30 m. These Darners feed on small insects, winged termites, and rarely on dragonflies which may be larger than themselves, such as King Skimmers. Females oviposit in wet wood a little above the waterline.

Fig. 28. Taper-tailed Darner, female. This captive specimen shows how the ovipositor blades would be used to lay eggs in soft wet wood in nature.

SPOTTED DARNERS
Genus *Boyeria*

Two species of this genus occur in North America, both in the east. The Fawn Darner occurs from Florida northward, the Ocellated Darner (*Boyeria grafiana*) is found from northern Georgia northward. These similar species have 2 yellow spots on each side of the thorax, a pattern not found in any other North American Darner.

Fig. 29. Fawn Darner, male.

FAWN DARNER

Boyeria vinosa

Identification: Common, size large, 60-71 mm (2.4-2.8 in).

    This Darner is brown, with 2 round yellow spots on each side of the thorax, and rows of yellow dots on the abdomen. The eyes are olive green to pale green. Each wing has a small dark brown spot at the base, and becomes tinted brown during ageing.

Ecology: The Fawn Darner ranges south to near Lake Okeechobee, and north to Nova Scotia, Quebec, and northern Ontario, west to Wisconsin, Missouri, and eastern Texas. Its habitat is shady, forested rivulets, streams, and rivers. The recorded flight season in Florida is May 11 to December 4.

Behavior: During most of the day this species usually hangs under twigs in dense forest under-growth. It has the peculiar habit of swinging its body gently forward and back a few times just after alighting, which may resemble the swaying of a twig in a breeze. Males are usually seen as they search for females by fluttering close along the bank in the shade for long distances. They usually patrol in the afternoon or evening, but often not until the last half hour before nightfall, when their patrols are reduced to about 3-7 m in length. Williamson wrote in 1907 (p. 144) "... its tendency to examine critically every object projecting above the water often makes its cap-ture an embarassing matter to the collector. More than once as I waited for an approaching male that insect suddenly left the line of flight I had mapped out for it, flew to within an inch of my legs, circled around one leg a time or two, then the other, then about both, and then quietly resumed its flight along the stream, oblivious to the net which had been frantically fanned all around it." Mating pairs hang in the forest understory within 20 m of the water. Females oviposit in wet wood or algae from below the waterline to as much as 25 cm above it.

CLUBTAILS
Family Gomphidae

These are very distinctive dragonflies. Clubtails get their name from the enlarged end of the abdomen in most species. The club is usually larger in males, and they often raise and display it like a flag. Clubtails generally have a camouflage pattern, usually brown or black marked with yellow in juveniles, the yellow becoming green after a few days. These dragonflies have widely spaced eyes as in the Petaltail Family, but do not have an ovipositor with blades. They perch horizontally on the ground, a leaf, or in some species, on stem tips. Clubtails do not soar, feed in swarms, or oviposit in tandem.

Fig. 30. Dragonhunter, female.

DRAGONHUNTERS
Genus *Hagenius*

Only one species of Dragonhunter occurs in North America, where it is the largest Club-tail on the continent. These dragonflies commonly hunt and eat other dragonflies.

DRAGONHUNTER

Hagenius brevistylus

Identification: Common, size very large, 77-87 mm (3.0-3.4 in) long.

This spectacular insect is black with bright yellow markings, including 2 stripes on each side of the thorax. The head is small with green eyes, and the legs and the wings are long. The male abdominal club is widest at the end, and is carried curved downward in a J shape during flight.

Ecology: The Dragonhunter ranges south to near Lake Okeechobee, north to Nova Scotia, and west to eastern Manitoba, Kansas, and central Texas. Its habitat is generally streams and rivers in Florida. The recorded Florida flight season is April 16 to November 8.

Behavior: This species eats other dragonflies up to the size of the Cyrano Darner, as well as other large insects such as swallowtail butterflies. Away from water it is wary and furtive, skulking near cover on the ground, or on tree limbs or twigs. At water some individuals are not wary, and perch on twigs or leaves with a commanding view. Mating is almost never seen, but one result of it is that the male's terminal abdominal appendages punch several holes in the female's head, damage whose purpose, if any, is unexplained. Females have several methods of ovipositing: they may swoop rythmically to the water near the bank, fly over open water while tapping the surface at intervals, or hover near the bank and drop eggs from the air.

Fig. 31. Clearlake Clubtail, male.

COMMON CLUBTAILS
Genus *Gomphus*

The term common applies to many of the species in this group, but not to all. The genus includes the species left over when the rest of the Clubtails were classified. An interesting feature of the female legs is that the spines on the hindlegs are much larger than those of males, which seems to adapt females for capturing larger prey. Only 4 of the 36 North American species occur in the Florida Peninsula.

CLEARLAKE CLUBTAIL   *Gomphus australis*

Identification: Uncommon, medium sized, 47-55 mm (1.9-2.2 in) long.

This species has a narrow abdominal club with a distinctively long segment 9 which is much longer than either segment 8 or segment 7. The face has a narrow brown cross-stripe, the eyes are blue-green to dark green, the legs are black, and abdominal segments 9 and 10 are usually black dorsally.

Ecology: The Clearlake Clubtail is an inhabitant of sand-bottomed lakes south to Palm Beach. It ranges on the Coastal Plain from Mississippi to North Carolina. It is an early spring species with a short flight season, recorded March 14 to April 27 in Florida.

Behavior: The whereabouts of this dragonfly away from water are not known. Males at water perch with the abdomen slightly raised and arched, preferably on lily pads, but sometimes on logs, shoreline sand, or grass. Occasionally they rest horizontally on the bulging bases of Bald Cypress trees. Females hover next to emergent vegetation, swooping down at intervals of several seconds to deposit batches of eggs.

Fig. 32. Cypress Clubtail, male.

CYPRESS CLUBTAIL

Gomphus minutus

Identification: Common, medium sized, 41-48 mm (1.6-1.9 in) long.

The thorax is dull green with brown stripes, the abdomen is brown with a full length yellow dorsal stripe and yellow sides on the club. Abdominal segment 9 is no longer than either segment 7 or segment 8. The eyes are gray, becoming blue-gray with age. The male dorsal terminal abdominal appendages have a ventral blade-like keel but no lateral teeth. The upper rear edge of the female head is distinctly concave.

The Sandhill Clubtail is very similar but is a little smaller, 37-45 mm (1.5-1.8 in) long, and has a brown facial cross-stripe. The male dorsal terminal abdominal appendages each have a large lateral tooth, while the upper rear margin of the female head is straight.

Ecology: The Cypress Clubtail ranges south to near Lake Okeechobee, and north to southeastern South Carolina. It is a spring species, recorded flying in Florida from February 14 to May 23. Its habitat is usually slow streams and rivers, but includes forest rivulets, lakes, and ponds. While it is not found on clear-water sand-bottomed lakes, it is occasionally found with the Sandhill Clubtail at brown-water sandy lakes margined with Bald Cypress swamp. There the Cypress Clubtail is dominant to the Sandhill Clubtail, and may exclude the latter from the water at times.

Behavior: The Cypress Clubtail perches on the ground or low plants, but roosts at night in the trees. It is one of the few dragonflies that has been seen eating the infamous "love-bug," a distasteful black fly, and may attack prey up to 5 m away. When disturbed, it occasionally flies in fast vertical 1 or 2 m undulations that make it difficult to keep in sight. Most mating occurs in fields, with the pair perched on a weed or on the ground for more than 15 minutes. The males apparently do not return to the water until late in their lives, so less mating occurs there than in most other dragonflies. Males perch on shore or sometimes on floating or emergent vegetation, from where they launch fast smooth patrols, the abdomen raised 40 degrees but with the tip bent downward. Females fly about 10 cm over the water either near the shore or in mid-stream and dip clusters of eggs into the water at about 3 second intervals, often hovering between dips.

42

Fig. 33. Sandhill Clubtail, male.

SANDHILL CLUBTAIL
Gomphus cavillaris

Identification: Common. See Identification of the very similar Cypress Clubtail.

Ecology: This species occurs south to near Lake Okeechobee as the subspecies *G. cavillaris cavillaris*. Another darker subspecies, *G. cavillaris brimleyi*, occurs in the Florida Panhandle and in southeastern North Carolina. The habitat is sand-bottomed lakes. It is a spring species, with a recorded Florida flight season of January 20 to May 24.

Behavior: The Sandhill Clubtail forages from the ground, and its prey includes damselflies and small beetles. Males perch on shore, floating objects, the bases of cypress trees, or waterside vegetation. They make short patrols lasting up to about 30 seconds close to shore with the body elevated 40 degrees. Mating takes about 20 minutes while the pair perches on low vegetation. Females deposit eggs by tapping the water during a fast, low, irregular flight.

Fig. 34. Blackwater Clubtail, male.

BLACKWATER CLUBTAIL

Gomphus dilatatus

Identification: Common, size large, 60-74 mm (2.4-2.9 in) long.

    This splendid dragonfly has a very wide flattened club on the mostly black abdomen, and black stripes on the gray-green thorax. Abdominal segments 8 to 10 are black with small pale green to yellow lateral spots on segments 8 and 9. The face is mostly black; the eyes are dark green (gray in juveniles).

Ecology: The Blackwater Clubtail generally inhabits blackwater (tannin-stained) rivers and streams south to near Lake Okeechobee. It ranges in the coastal states from eastern Louisiana to North Carolina. The recorded Florida flight season is March 3 to August 27, but it is most common in late spring.

Behavior: Away from water this species perches on the ground, logs, or leaves. Its prey includes grasshoppers, damselflies, and dragonflies up to the size of a King Skimmer. Males usually perch on leaves over the water, but may also perch on logs or the bank. Needham and Heywood (1929, p. 97) gave this written image of a patrolling male: "The adult goes steaming along in steady horizontal flight two or three feet above the open river with tail aloft, and wings scarcely showing vibration. It is a striking figure. The slender middle part of the abdomen is inclined upward and the broadly dilated end segments are held parallel with the course of flight, but at a higher level than that of the bulky striped thorax. Back and forth it goes, steadily, easily, as ruler of the lesser life over the open stream." However, males generally do not exert themselves that much, and spend most of their time perching. Mating occurs in the tree tops. Females oviposit quickly, with fast dashes to the water at several points a few m apart.

HANGING CLUBTAILS
Genus *Stylurus*

    These Clubtails fly mostly in late summer and autumn. Males have a moderately clubbed abdomen but the female abdomen is nearly cylindrical. The front of the thorax is dark with 2 iso-

44

Fig. 35. Shining Clubtail, male.

lated pale stripes which are divergent downward. The legs are short. They commonly perch on the tops of tree leaves which their weight bends downward until they are hanging nearly vertically and facing the sky. Only 2 of the 11 North American species are found in the Florida Peninsula.

SHINING CLUBTAIL
Stylurus ivae

Identification: Northern Florida, uncommon, medium sized, 50-61 mm (2.0-2.4 in) long.

The face, eyes, and sides of the thorax are mostly yellow-green, while the abdominal club is largely pale orange.

The Russet-tipped Clubtail has a gray-green thorax and rusty orange abdominal club.

Ecology: The Shining Clubtail occurs south only to Gainesville. It ranges in the Coastal Plain from Alabama to North Carolina. The species begins adult emergence later than any other Florida dragonfly, with a recorded flight season of September 1 to November 19. Its habitat is sand-bottomed streams and rivers.

Behavior: This species forages in sunny clearings and along forest edges, perching on leaves of weeds, bushes, or trees. Williamson in 1932 (p. 17) wrote: "They rested usually on tree leaves, always in sun, and were not wild or nervous. Coming out of the forest they appeared on the stream, a bright dash of brilliant yellow as conspicuous and lovely as a goldfinch." Males at water perch on overhanging leaves or on sticks or logs in the water. During cool weather they may be active only for a couple of hours in the warmest part of the afternoon. Patrolling males at a distance may appear to be two shining spots moving together (the thorax and the abdominal club). They hover more, fly lower, and shift positions less often and more slowly than patrolling male Russet-tipped Clubtails. The patrols often cover 30 m of stream. Mating pairs hang in trees near the stream. A female perches inconspicuously on streamside tree leaves until she accumulates a ball of eggs, then flies out to lay the eggs with one or two taps to the water before perching and forming another egg ball.

45

Fig. 36. Russet-tipped Clubtail, male.

RUSSET-TIPPED CLUBTAIL
Stylurus plagiatus

Identification: Common, medium sized, 53-66 mm (2.1-2.6 in) long.

The thorax is gray-green with black stripes, the slender abdomen bears a rusty orange club. The face is brown, the eyes are dark green, and the legs are short.

The Southeastern Spinyleg looks quite similar, but is larger and has a green face and long legs. The Shining Clubtail is much paler, with a yellow-green thorax and pale orange abdominal club. The Two-striped Forceptail has a mostly brown thorax.

Ecology: The Russet-tipped Clubtail breeds in rivers, streams, and lakes south to Palm Beach. It ranges north to New York, and west to Michigan, Oklahoma, and southern California. It also occurs in northern Mexico, and Pelee Island, Ontario (if the species still occurs in Lake Erie). Its recorded Florida flight season is April 21 to December 1, but it is most common in the autumn.

Behavior: This Clubtail forages from leaves along forest edges and in treetops. Males patrol widely over open water with the abdomen raised 25 degrees. Mating occurs on weed stems or in trees, and in warm weather patrolling and mating may occur from 9 A.M. until nightfall. Females oviposit in a fast low irregular flight, touching the water at intervals of several m, or they may perch between sets of only 1 or 2 dips to the water.

Fig. 37. Southeastern Spinyleg, male.

SPINYLEGS
Genus *Dromogomphus*

The 2 species of this genus that occur in Florida are very differently colored, but both exhibit the main feature of the genus which is long hind legs with long ventral spines on the basal halves (i.e. on the femora). The head is proportionately small. The third species of the genus, the Flag-tailed Spinyleg (*Dromogomphus spoliatus*), is found north and west of Florida.

SOUTHEASTERN SPINYLEG   *Dromogomphus armatus*

Identification: Northern Florida, rare, size large, 63-68 mm (2.5-2.7 in) long.

The thorax is green with black stripes; the male abdominal club is rusty orange and compressed vertically. The female club is narrow and marked with pale green to rusty brown. The face has a brown cross-line, the eyes are green, and the legs are long.

The Russet-tipped Clubtail is smaller with short legs, and the male abdominal club is flattened horizontally.

Ecology: This fine dragonfly is found south to Tampa. It ranges in the coastal states from Mississippi to North Carolina. This species, very particular about its habitat, prefers small spring-fed streams with clear water flowing over deep muck. The recorded flight season in Florida is June 9 to November 20, but it is most common in late summer.

Behavior: This Clubtail away from water may be very wary, perching on the ground, low plants, or tree leaves. It often flies within cover. Males perch horizontally on sticks or plants over the water. If no perches overhang the water they rest on bushes back from the shore. When disturbed they fly wildly over a wide area before selecting another perch. Females hover about 50 cm up near the edge of vegetation, then repeatedly dash to the water to lay eggs.

Fig. 38. Black-shouldered Spinyleg, mature male.

BLACK-SHOULDERED SPINYLEG
Dromogomphus spinosus

Identification: Common, medium sized, 54-67 mm (2.1-2.6 in) long.

The thorax is pale yellow in juveniles, becoming pale green at maturity, with wide black shoulder stripes. The abdomen is black, with a slender club in males, and with a pale green dorsal stripe on at least segments 1 to 7. The eyes are gray in juveniles, becoming dark green at maturity. In Florida the face usually has a wide black cross-band. The legs are long and black.

Ecology: This species occurs south to near Lake Okeechobee, and north to Maine, southern Quebec, southern Ontario, and Minnesota, west to Kansas and western Texas. In Florida its habitat is generally rivers and streams, where it has been recorded flying from April 14 to November 11. The larvae can survive a certain degree of pollution, unlike most other Clubtails.

Behavior: The Black-shouldered Spinyleg forages along forest margins or in fairly dense forest, often flying through cover rather than around it. It perches on the leaves of trees or bushes, or on the ground, feeding on butterflies, damselflies, medium sized dragonflies, and other insects. Males perch on leaves over the water, on logs, on rocks, or on the bare shore. They make large irregular patrols over the water, hovering occasionally with the abdomen raised. They appear larger than they really are due to the long legs folded under the thorax during flight. Mating pairs perch high in trees. Females fly fast figure-8's low over the water, dropping the abdomen at intervals to touch the surface and deposit eggs.

Fig. 39. Black-shouldered Spinyleg, juvenile female.

Fig. 40. Gray-green Clubtail, male.

POND CLUBTAILS
Genus *Arigomphus*

Only 1 of the 7 species in this North American genus is found in Florida. Unlike most other Clubtails, these dragonflies are capable of breeding in still water, including ponds. Females are the only North American Clubtails with ovipositors.

GRAY-GREEN CLUBTAIL   *Arigomphus pallidus*

Identification: Common, medium sized, 51-62 mm (2.0-2.4 in) long.

This dragonfly has a gray-green thorax with only faint brown stripes. The abdomen is mostly gray-green, with segments 8 and 9 of the slender club brown, a pale segment 10, and pale terminal appendages. The eyes are green. This is a bulldog among dragonflies, for its head is large and its legs are thick and strong. The female has an ovipositor, a pointed spout-like device under abdominal segment 9.

Ecology: The Gray-green Clubtail occurs throughout the Florida Peninsula. It ranges in the Coastal Plain from Alabama to South Carolina. The recorded flight season in Florida is March 20 to October 11. It apparently has two peaks of adult emergence, a major one in the spring and a minor one in late summer, but it is scarce in late June and July. The habitat is lakes, stream backwaters, and permanent ponds.

Behavior: Away from water this species perches on the ground or low vegetation, or sometimes in trees. They hover and skulk through heavy vegetation, an especially notable behavior in females, and eat insects up to the size of medium sized dragonflies. The rather wary males perch on shore or low shoreline vegetation with the abdomen bent down at the tip. Mating pairs perch on bushes or on the ground. Ovipositing females fly slowly or hover near vegetation, dropping about every 2 seconds to the water surface to release a batch of eggs. Sometimes they hover to oviposit in wavelets at the edge of a lake.

Fig. 41. Common Sanddragon, pair in mating wheel. Male holds female head with his terminal abdominal appendages while female receives stored sperm from genitalia under male's second abdominal segment.

SANDDRAGONS
Genus *Progomphus*

These medium sized dragonflies are our only Clubtails with definite wing markings, a small brown spot at the base of each wing. They are mostly brown with a slender slightly clubbed abdomen and short legs. These dragonflies are associated with sand which their larvae require for burrowing. Four species of the genus occur in North America, with 2 in the Florida Peninsula.

COMMON SANDDRAGON   *Progomphus obscurus*

Identification: Northern Florida, common, medium sized, 43-56 mm (1.7-2.2 in) long.

The thorax has yellow frontal stripes and white lateral stripes, while the slender abdomen has a line of dorsal yellow triangles on segments 2 to 7. Segments 8 to 10 have only small or obscure pale lateral spots, but the terminal abdominal appendages are yellow. There is a small brown spot at the base of each wing, and the legs are short. The eyes are greenish yellow in males, brown in females.

The very similar Tawny Sanddragon is a somewhat larger lake species, 49-57 mm (2.0-2.3 in) long, which has abdominal segment 8 mottled with large lateral yellow blotches. The eyes are olive tan, and the dorsal abdominal markings in females are orange.

Ecology: The Common Sanddragon occurs south only to Gainesville, but ranges north to New Hampshire, Ohio, Michigan, and Wisconsin, and west to Wyoming, eastern Colorado, and western Texas. Its habitat in Florida is sand-bottomed streams and rivers. The recorded Florida flight season is April 2 to August 7.

Behavior: Away from water this species perches horizontally on weed or twig tips up into the tree tops. Males usually perch on the sand near the water with abdomens tilted upward 45-60 degrees. On hot days they may practically stand on their heads in an extreme obelisk position. Sometimes they hover over midstream with raised abdomens. Mating pairs perch on weeds or trees or on the ground near the water for about 15 minutes. Females have 2 methods of oviposi-

51

Fig. 42. Tawny Sanddragon, male.

tion. Most commonly they fly low and fast over moving water while tapping the surface here and there. Sometimes they hover near the edge of a riffle with the end of the abdomen bent slightly downward and spray their dry round eggs into the water. The male may guard the female, and is the only Clubtail known at present to do this.

TAWNY SANDDRAGON   *Progomphus alachuensis*

Identification: Common. See Identification of the similar Common Sanddragon.

Ecology: This species occurs in the Florida Peninsula south to near Lake Okeechobee, but is not found anywhere else. It breeds in sand-bottomed lakes, where it has a recorded flight season of April 10 to August 30.

Behavior: Away from water these dragonflies perch horizontally or in the obelisk position on weed tips or on the ground. At water the males perch alertly with an elevated abdomen, usually on sandy shores. Their flight is a little higher, slower, and smoother than that of the Common Sanddragon. Females oviposit during a low fast erratic flight with quick dips to the water, or they may apparently drop eggs during a slow hovering flight from 30 cm up.

Fig. 43. Two-striped Forceptail, male.

FORCEPTAILS
Genus *Aphylla*

Of the 3 North American species in this genus, only 1 occurs in Florida. Males have forceps-like dorsal terminal abdominal appendages, and differ from all other North American dragonflies due to their lack of the ventral terminal abdominal appendage.

TWO-STRIPED FORCEPTAIL   *Aphylla williamsoni*

Identification: Common, size large, 65-73 mm (2.6-2.9 in) long.

This dragonfly has a distinctive color pattern on the dark brown thorax, including a yellow W on the front and 2 greenish yellow stripes on each side. A third narrow lateral pale stripe may be present between the 2 others, most often in females. The abdomen is slender, with segments 8 to 10 rufous, but segment 8 has a wide yellow to orange flange in males, a narrow one in females. The yellow face has brown cross-stripes, the eyes are blue-gray, the legs are short, and the stigmas are pale tan. The male lacks a ventral terminal abdominal appendage. He grips the female thorax during mating with his forceps-like dorsal abdominal appendages.

Ecology: The Two-striped Forceptail occurs throughout the Florida Peninsula. It ranges in the Coastal Plain from Louisiana to Virginia. Its habitat is lakes, permanent ponds, and slow parts of streams, all with mucky bottoms. The recorded flight season in Florida is April 7 to November 2.

Behavior: This species apparently forages mostly in tree tops, but is sometimes found in brushy fields or among woodland shrubs. Males perch warily on low waterside vegetation, or occasionally on the bank, with the abdomen raised about 20 degrees. They occasionally patrol over open water until sundown in warm weather. Mating pairs perch on low vegetation or in trees well back from the water. Females oviposit mostly about 8:00 to 8:30 P.M. using 3 different methods. They may hover near shore vegetation and swoop rhythmically to the water at 2 second intervals, or fly a rapid irregular pattern over open water while tapping the surface at points 2 to 3 m apart, or apparently they may also drop eggs while hovering over the water near vegetation.

53

Fig. 44. Say's Spiketail, male.

SPIKETAILS
Family Cordulegastridae

Only one genus of this family occurs in North America.

Genus *Cordulegaster*

These insects are unique, even by dragonfly standards. Our species are large and black with yellow markings, and their green or blue eyes meet at one point on top of the head. Each side of the thorax has 2 pale stripes. Females have spike-like ovipositors used by hovering over shallow water and driving it vertically into the bottom in a motion resembling the thrusting of a sewing machine needle. During mating the ovipositor fits into a deep pocket in the base of the male's abdomen and thorax. Abdominal segments 9 and 10 of the female are soft and can accordion up when the ovipositor enters the bottom. Three of the 8 North American species occur in the Florida Peninsula, where they are found southward only to Gainesville.

SAY'S SPIKETAIL   *Cordulegaster sayi*

Identification: Northern Florida, rare, size large, 60-69 mm (2.4-2.7 in) long.

The only Spiketail in Florida with yellow rings around the abdomen. The eyes are gray-green, and the thorax has magenta markings. The female ovipositor barely extends beyond the tip of the abdomen. The species is named after Thomas Say, early American entomologist.

Ecology: This species is found south to Gainesville. It occurs only from northern Florida to central Georgia. The habitat is trickling hillside seepages in deciduous forest. The flight season is in the spring, recorded from February 27 to April 22.

Behavior: Say's Spiketail feeds near forest edges or in clearings, where it perches obliquely on weed stems. Its diet includes many wasps and wild bees which may be attacked from a distance of 5 m. Males patrol low over seepage areas during the middle of the day, hovering and perching often. Mating lasts for over an hour, and takes place while the pair perches on a stem or twig

Fig. 45. Twin-spotted Spiketail, female.

near the seeps or in the fields. Females oviposit in the early afternoon with the motions as described for the genus.

TWIN-SPOTTED SPIKETAIL   *Cordulegaster maculata*

Identification: Northern Florida, uncommon, size large, 64-76 mm (2.5-3.0 in) long.

The only Spiketail in Florida with rows of spots on the abdomen. It is dark brown, with aqua-blue eyes, 2 yellow stripes on each side of the thorax, and 2 rows of small pale yellow abdominal spots. The female ovipositor is very long, extending beyond the abdomen by the length of segments 9 + 10.

Brown Cruisers have only 1 lateral thoracic pale stripe, and very long legs. The Fawn Darner has 2 lateral thoracic spots instead of stripes.

Ecology: The Twin-spotted Spiketail occurs south only to Gainesville, but ranges north to Nova Scotia, northern Ontario, and Minnesota, and west to Arkansas and eastern Texas. The habitat is forest streams, and the species flies in early spring, recorded from February 22 to April 19 in Florida.

Behavior: This rather wary species feeds along forest edges, perching obliquely on weed stems or twigs. Prey includes bees and wasps. Males patrol long lengths of stream from about 9 A.M. to dusk, often with an abundance peak about 6 P.M. Pairs hang on a twig for the 50 minutes required for mating. Females oviposit as described for the genus, with a peak of activity in the evening. They stab the eggs vertically into a soft muck bottom, but thrust obliquely backward into a harder sand bottom.

Fig. 46. Arrowhead Spiketail, màle.

ARROWHEAD SPIKETAIL

Cordulegaster obliqua

Identification: Northern Florida, rare, size very large, 78-88 mm (3.1-3.5 in) long.

This is the only Florida dragonfly with a series of pale yellow arrowhead-shaped markings on the top of the abdomen. It is mostly black, with aqua-blue eyes and 2 yellow stripes on each side of the thorax. The female ovipositor projects about the length of abdominal segment 10 beyond the abdomen.

River Cruisers have only 1 yellow stripe on each side of the thorax, and have very long legs. The Dragonhunter has green separated eyes, long hind legs, and a clubbed abdomen.

Ecology: The Arrowhead Spiketail occurs south only to Gainesville, but ranges north to Maine, eastern Ontario, and Wisconsin, and west to Kansas and eastern Texas. The species is smaller in the northern part of its range, with brighter yellow markings and green eyes. The southern form, *fasciata*, ranges from Louisiana to North Carolina. The habitat is spring-fed muck-bottomed forest rivulets. The flight season is later than in our other Spiketails, recorded from May 25 to July 1 in Florida.

Behavior: Basically like the Twin-spotted Spiketail, so far as known. The Arrowhead often hunts among clumps of brush near a wall-like forest edge. Males patrol during the middle part of the day.

CRUISERS
Family Macromiidae

These are medium to large sized dragonflies, brown or black with yellow markings, that fly on stiff narrow wings built for sustained speed. A yellow belt around the thorax forms a single yellow stripe on each side, and the legs are very long and bear forked claws. The eyes are in contact on top of the head, and the face is dark with 2 yellow cross-stripes. Males cruise long distances along shorelines, and take their mates into the trees. Females lack ovipositors. They lay their green eggs by dragging their abdominal tips in the water during rapid forward flight, usually near a high or overhanging bank.

Fig. 47. Stream Cruiser, juvenile male.

BROWN CRUISERS
Genus *Didymops*

This genus includes 2 medium sized species, both found in Florida. Their coloration is non-metallic; the eyes are green at maturity and the body is brown with pale yellow markings. The front of the thorax lacks stripes, but abdominal segments 4 to 6 have pale (often interrupted) rings. These dragonflies fly in the early spring and perch obliquely on weed stems or twigs of bushes.

STREAM CRUISER   *Didymops transversa*

Identification: Northern Florida, common, medium sized, 51-60 mm (2.0-2.4 in) long.

The thorax is brown with 1 pale yellow stripe on each side, and the abdomen has pale yellow spots or bands on segments 1 to 8. Each wing has a small brown spot at the base, and the costa vein is brown. The eyes are brown in juveniles, changing eventually to glassy green, but the change is slow in females. The male has a conspicuously clubbed abdomen with yellow terminal appendages. The legs are long.

The Maidencane Cruiser is very similar, but is gray-brown and a little larger, 61-68 mm (2.4-2.7 in) long. It lacks brown spots at the wing bases and the costa veins are pale yellow. It is a sand- bottomed lake species, whereas in Florida the Stream Cruiser inhabits streams and rivers. Males of both species resemble a Clubtail in flight, but they hang rather than squat on a perch, and the eyes are in contact on top of the head.

Ecology: The Stream Cruiser is found south only to Gainesville, but it ranges north to Nova Scotia, Ontario, and Minnesota, and west to Illinois, Kansas, and central Texas. In Florida its habitat is streams and rivers, rarely lakes. The species flies in the spring, recorded in Florida from January 25 to May 11.

Behavior: This dragonfly feeds by flying low over fields, paths, or roads, or sometimes by hovering in spaces among weeds or forest underbrush. They perch obliquely on weed stems or hang

Fig. 48. Maidencane Cruiser, male.

beneath twigs. Males fly patrols up to 100 m in length along the shoreline, and can mate before their eyes change to green. Mated pairs hang on weeds, bushes, or low tree branches. Females fly fast and low over the water, touching the abdomen tip at intervals of about 2 m to wash off eggs.

MAIDENCANE CRUISER   *Didymops floridensis*

Identification: Common.
See Identification under Stream Cruiser.

Ecology: This species has been found only in Florida, where it ranges south to near Lake Okeechobee. Its habitat is sand-bottomed lakes edged with Maidencane grass, and often also with Bald Cypress trees. It flies in the spring, recorded from January 20 to May 3.

Behavior: The Maidencane Cruiser feeds by flying far and wide through woodlands and weedy clearings. It sometimes hovers among bushes while on the lookout for prey, or perches oblique-ly on weed stems. Males fly fast, long patrols along the edge of Maidencane or among Bald Cypress trees. Females also fly at high speed in the same areas, touching the tips of their ab-domens to the water to wash off eggs without slackening speed. They may select one cypress tree and rapidly circle its base many times, and when finished egg laying, they often grab a damself-ly and carry it to the trees to be eaten.

RIVER CRUISERS
Genus *Macromia*

These are splendid large dragonflies. The Florida species are metallic black marked with bright yellow, and the eyes are brilliant metallic green (red-brown in juveniles). The abdomen has yellow spots or rings, but unlike the Brown Cruisers the markings are spot-like instead of ring-like on segments 4 to 6. In our species the front of the thorax bears a pair of short yellow stripes. These dragonflies fly during the summer. They hang under tree twigs to perch, and rare-ly hover. Only 2 of the 8 North American species are found in the Florida Peninsula.

Fig. 49. Georgia River Cruiser, male.

GEORGIA RIVER CRUISER

Macromia georgina

Identification: Common, size large, 68-79 mm (2.7-3.1 in) long.

This beautiful black dragonfly has bright yellow markings, including 1 lateral thoracic stripe on each side, a complete yellow ring around abdominal segment 2, and yellow spots on segments 3 to 8, with a single large spot on segment 7. Males have clubbed abdomens. Females have a touch of brown at the base of each wing. The legs are long.

The Royal River Cruiser is similar, but larger, 74-91 mm (2.9-3.6 in) long, and has smaller abdominal spots. Abdominal segment 7 usually bears a pair of yellow spots, the yellow ring around segment 2 is interrupted dorsally, the male abdomen is not clubbed, and the female lacks brown at the wing bases.

Spiketails have 2 pale stripes on each side of the thorax, shorter legs, and the eyes barely touch on top of the head. The Dragonhunter has 2 yellow lateral thoracic stripes, a yellow face, a striped abdomen, separated eyes, and it perches horizontally.

Ecology: The Georgia River Cruiser ranges south to near Lake Okeechobee, and north to New Jersey and southern Illinois, west to Kansas and Texas. Its habitat is rivers and streams. The recorded flight season in Florida is May 11 to November 9.

Behavior: This species feeds by flying long distances along roads and through open forest at any height, but individuals sometimes soar high with swarms of other dragonflies. Males fly on long patrols along the shore at a height of about 20 cm, beginning early in the morning in warm weather, and are most active in the morning. Patrolling males usually fly fast, but if they fly slower it is with alternate flits and sails on raised wings. Mating pairs hang high in the trees. Females fly swiftly along the bank, tapping the abdomen periodically on the water to wash off eggs. Ovipositing females commonly go back and forth along an area where the bank is steep or over-hung with branches.

Fig. 50. Royal River Cruiser, male.

ROYAL RIVER CRUISER   *Macromia taeniolata*

Identification: Common, size very large.

See Identification of the similar Georgia River Cruiser.

Ecology: The Royal River Cruiser ranges south to Naples, and north to Delaware, Pennsylvania, Ohio, and Michigan, west to Illinois, Iowa, and eastern Texas. The habitat of this magnificent insect is rivers, streams, and sometimes lakes. The recorded Florida flight season is April 14 to November 23.

Behavior: Like that of the Georgia River Cruiser, except that males patrolling over water fly higher and slower, and spend more time along the bank. Rarely, males will hover low over aquatic weeds. Females oviposit for about 2 minutes, mostly in the afternoon.

EMERALDS
Family Corduliidae

These are brown dragonflies, many with brilliant emerald green jewel-like eyes. Some also have green or bronze metallic iridescence on the body. The eyes are in contact on top of the head, and the female either lacks an ovipositor or has one shaped like a spout. Many species are difficult to observe because they fly only briefly in the spring, or for only a short time each day, or breed in rare types of aquatic habitats.

BASKETTAILS
Genus *Epitheca*

These are medium to large sized brown dragonflies with little metallic coloration, and with a yellow lateral stripe on each side of the abdomen. A small yellow dot is present on each side of the thorax, and the face is usually yellow but may be brown. Males have a spindle-shaped abdomen which is widest at segment 6, while females have a parallel-sided abdomen. These dragonflies are exceptionally quick and agile on the wing. The name Baskettail refers to the fact that females carry a whole clutch of their yellow to orange eggs using a long split plate (subgenital plate) under abdominal segment 9. Thus all of their eggs are "in one basket." Note that females carrying egg balls can be mistaken for Clubtails. This egg ball when deposited with a quick double dip on a nearly submerged plant unravels into a gelatinous rope about 15 cm long containing several hundred eggs. The value of this oviposition method is twofold: the female has to expose herself only once to aquatic predators, and the eggs are placed near the water surface where the higher oxygen content and temperature speed embryological development. When many females select the same place to deposit egg ropes, large masses can be formed.

Our Baskettails include the large and distinctive Prince Baskettail, and 4 similar medium sized species collectively called the small Baskettails in the discussions below. Some scientists place the Prince in the genus *Epicordulia*, and the smaller species in the genus *Tetragoneuria*. What sparrows are to the bird watcher, — small, brown, and difficult to identify — so are the small Baskettails to the dragonfly watcher! Four other Baskettail species, all of the small Baskettail type, occur in North America.

Fig. 51. Egg ropes of Baskettails. Many females have laid gelatinous ropes filled with eggs at one spot. Fresh ropes are pale, old ones have become green due to algae invading the jelly.

Fig. 52. Prince Baskettail, male.

PRINCE BASKETTAIL

Epitheca princeps

Identification: Common, size large, 70-80 mm (2.8-3.2 in) long.

This is the largest of the Baskettails, and the only one with brown wingtips. The Prince is a slender brown dragonfly with large brown spots at the base, middle, and tip of each wing. The eyes are red-brown in juveniles, becoming bronzy brown in females and metallic green in males.

This species patrols like a Darner, and is as large as a Darner, but no North American Darner has large brown wing spots. The only other Florida dragonflies with a similar wing pattern are certain Skimmers, but these are all much smaller, and perch at regular short intervals on weed stems. The Prince is seldom seen perching, but when it does it hangs under a twig of a tree, often with the wings somewhat raised.

Ecology: The Prince Baskettail occurs throughout the Florida Peninsula, and ranges north to Maine, southern Quebec, southern Ontario, and Minnesota, west to Nebraska and Texas. In the northern part of its range it is much smaller with reduced wing spots. The southeastern form, which may be called the variety *regina*, ranges in the coastal states from Louisiana to Virginia. The habitat in Florida is rivers, streams, and lakes, or occasionally ponds. The recorded Florida flight season is March 15 to December 3.

Behavior: This species usually flies over the trees when foraging, but may form feeding swarms at any level in the evening. It eats mostly small insects but also takes large mayflies. Patrolling males are conspicuous as they fly hour after hour about 2 m up with a leisurely flight. A few beats of the wings are followed by a short sail on slightly raised wings, with occasionally a swift dash at another dragonfly as much as 20 m away. Male patrols are about 20-30 m wide and up to 70 m long, from near shore to well out over open water. Williamson wrote in 1902 (p. 124): "In the gray twilight, before sunrise, ...*princeps*, misty and indistinct, floated by. After sunset, when we went to the shore..., there he was again, out over the water, hurrying along in the gathering dusk as though his day were not yet completed." Females are seldom seen except for brief visits to the water for mating and oviposition. Mating may take place at any time of day and pairs fly for long distances along the shoreline before hanging in a tree. Females oviposit mostly in the evening.

Fig. 53. Common Baskettail, male. Many specimens nearly lack the brown basal wing spots.

They are striking in appearance, with the orange egg ball poised on the end of the slender abdomen which is curled vertically upward. The egg rope is about 50 cm long after it is draped over a leaf or stem awash at the water surface.

COMMON BASKETTAIL   *Epitheca cynosura*

Identification: Common, medium sized, 36-44 mm (1.4-1.7 in) long.

A brown dragonfly with yellow lateral abdominal stripes. Many individuals have a large brown triangular spot at the base of each hindwing, and those specimens are easily identified. The eyes are red-brown in juveniles, usually developing a metallic green band across the front at maturity. Many Common Baskettails have a rather stout abdomen. The female terminal abdominal appendages are short.

When examined in the hand, the male dorsal terminal abdominal appendages have a ventral angle in side view, with a ventral keel extending posteriorly from it. There is also a lateral keel on each appendage, and the side of the appendage between the keels is flat. The forewing stigma of both sexes is less than 2.46 mm long, the length of abdominal segment 6 in both sexes is 2.6 times its width, or less. The female terminal abdominal appendages are 1.42-2.26 mm long; the female subgenital plate has either parallel or convergent forks.

Similar dragonflies with prominent basal spots in the hindwings lack prominent yellow sides on the abdomen, except that the female Marl Pennant has most of the abdomen yellow, but that species perches horizontally on stem tips.

Those Common Baskettails with only a touch of brown at the base of each hindwing can not ordinarily be separated from other small Baskettails without capture and microscopic examination. These species can be separated according to the following notes:

1) **Stripe-winged Baskettail** — Females with a brown stripe along the front edge of each wing are distinctive and easily identified. Females with clear wings can be identified by noting that the terminal abdominal appendages are longer than in our other female small Baskettails, as long as abdominal segments 9 + 10. The male has a slender abdomen.

The male dorsal terminal abdominal appendage is similar to that of the male Common Baskettail, but is longer (3.4 mm or more), lacks a ventral keel, and is swollen or convex on the side. The ventral angle projects downward and inward. The female terminal abdominal appendages are 2.21-3.72 mm long, the female forewing stigma is less than 2.65 mm long. The female subgenital plate is like that of the female Common Baskettail.

2) **Sepia Baskettail** – This species has no green in the eyes, the thorax is olive yellow, and the yellow lateral abdominal stripes are wide. The male appears reddish brown with a stubby tapered abdomen, and usually patrols over water in the late afternoon and evening. The Sepia is the only small Baskettail in Florida whose flight season extends into the late summer.

The male is distinguished by its long ventral terminal abdominal appendage, 78% or more as long as the dorsal appendages (74% or less in our other small Baskettails). The female has no brown whatsoever at the base of the hindwing, and has straight forks on the subgenital plate.

3) **Florida Baskettail** – The abdomen is long, slender, and parallel-sided. The only other small Baskettail south of Lake Okeechobee is the Sepia.

The male dorsal terminal abdominal appendage is similar to that of the male Common Baskettail, but has no ventral angle in direct side view. The forewing stigmas are long, 2.27-2.77 mm in males, and 2.33-3.02 mm in females. The length of abdominal segment 6 is 3.5-4 times longer than its width, reflecting the slenderness of the abdomen. The female terminal abdominal appendages are 1.89-2.33 mm long, the subgenital plate is like that of the female Common Baskettail.

Ecology: The Common Baskettail ranges south to near Lake Okeechobee, north to Nova Scotia, southern Ontario, and Minnesota, and west into Nebraska and Texas. The habitat is most sorts of permanent quiet waters such as lakes, ponds, marshes, swamps, and slow streams and rivers. Larvae can tolerate some organic pollution. The flight season, primarily in the spring, is recorded from January 8 to May 7 in Florida. However, near Gainesville another flight season occurs from October 3 until the first frosts.

Behavior: This species feeds with a fast erratic flight, often in swarms containing both sexes, on prey as large as winged termites. It perches occasionally on weed stems or twigs with the body at an oblique angle to the ground. Males continuously patrol about 3 to 10 m of shoreline at a height of 1/2 to 1 m, often hovering in one spot for minutes at a time. The territories are often above a patch of algae or submerged vegetation. They may patrol most of the day but usually reach a peak of activity in late afternoon. Mating takes place in flight, and the pair usually flies in one direction for the 5 minutes required, so that long distances are covered. Females form an egg ball while perching on a twig, then deposit it as described for the genus, usually in the afternoon.

Kormondy (1959) studied the ecology of this species.

Fig. 54. Stripe-winged Baskettail, female. Most females and all males lack the wing stripes, but note the long female terminal abdominal appendages.

STRIPE-WINGED BASKETTAIL   *Epitheca costalis*

Identification: Northern Florida, fairly common, medium sized.

See Identification of the very similar Common Baskettail.

Ecology: The Stripe-winged Baskettail is found south to Orlando, but ranges north to North Carolina, Tennessee, and southern Illinois, west to Missouri, Arkansas, and Texas. It also ranges north along the coast to New Jersey. The usual habitat in Florida is clear- water sand-bottomed lakes, but it can also breed in stream pools. The flight season is early spring, recorded from January 20 to April 18 in Florida.

Behavior: So far as known, like that of the Common Baskettail, except that male patrols are a little larger, and mating pairs leave the water to perch on a weed stem for about 10 minutes.

Fig. 55. Sepia Baskettail, male.

SEPIA BASKETTAIL   *Epitheca sepia*

Identification: Common, medium sized.

This species has no brown at the base of the hindwings, except for a mere trace in some males. See Identification of the very similar Common Baskettail.

Ecology: The Sepia Baskettail is found throughout the Florida Peninsula, and north into Georgia and Alabama. It inhabits slow streams, and both sand-bottomed and mud-bottomed lakes. It flies from March 3 to November 23, but is most common in the spring.

Behavior: This species commonly feeds with a fast erratic flight at dusk. Males patrol about 10 m of shoreline from late afternoon to dusk at a height of about 30 cm. Females lay eggs at dusk.

Paulson (1973) gave some notes on this species.

Fig. 56. Florida Baskettail, male.

FLORIDA BASKETTAIL

Epitheca stella

Identification: Common, medium sized.

See Identification under Common Baskettail.

Ecology: The Florida Baskettail, apparently endemic to Florida, ranges throughout the peninsula. In southern Florida it inhabits almost any type of pond, but in northern Florida it prefers semi-fertile lakes edged with sawgrass. It has also been found at slow streams. The flight season is in early spring, from February 2 to April 25.

Behavior: So far as known, like the Common Baskettail, except that pairs perch to complete mating. Females oviposit in the early afternoon.

Paulson (1973) gave some notes on this species.

STRIPED EMERALDS
Genus *Somatochlora*

These are medium sized dragonflies, slender and elegant, but mostly metallic brown. They are not common, and they often fly high when feeding. Of the 26 North American species, only 2 occur in peninsular Florida. One of these has white stripes on the sides of the thorax, the other lacks thoracic stripes. Females of our species have a trough-like or spout-like ovipositor underneath abdominal segment 9.

Fig. 57. Mocha Emerald, mature male.

MOCHA EMERALD
Somatochlora linearis

Identification: Northern Florida, uncommon, medium sized, 56-70 mm (2.2-2.8 in) long.

A slender, dark metallic brown dragonfly with brown-tinted wings. Juveniles have a pale spot on each side of abdominal segment 2 that becomes obscured at maturity. The eyes are red-brown in juveniles and females, becoming brilliant metallic green in males. The female has a slender, pointed, spout-like ovipositor under abdominal segment 9.

The Twilight Darner is larger and paler brown, with broad wings and less metallic eyes.

Ecology: The Mocha Emerald ranges south to Orlando, and north to Massachusetts, New York, and Michigan, west to Kansas and Texas. Its habitat is small forest streams, including those which partially dry up in summer. The recorded Florida flight season is May 11 to September 2.

Behavior: This species usually feeds 7 to 10 m up over roads or clearings, but may also hunt by hovering in forest undergrowth. When traveling it often flies with rapid 1 m up-and-down and side-to-side undulations, but at other times the flight may be more leisurely with considerable gliding. It perches nearly vertically on twigs, or occasionally on tree trunks, in forest shade most of the day. It is most active in the early morning and from late afternoon to dusk. Males patrol about 20-30 m of stream 1 m above the water, frequently hovering for several seconds at a time. Mating pairs hang from twigs near the stream. A female flies low along the edge of a stream, swinging her abdomen downward to use the ovipositor like a pick to poke eggs into mud, sand, or fine gravel.

Williamson (1922) gave some notes on this species.

Fig. 58. Fine-lined Emerald, mature male.

FINE-LINED EMERALD   *Somatochlora filosa*

Identification: Uncommon, medium-sized, 52-69 mm (2.1-2.7 in) long.

This slender dragonfly has a dark metallic green thorax with 2 narrow white stripes on each side, and a dark metallic brown abdomen. The eyes are brown-red in juveniles, becoming brilliant metallic green at maturity. The female has a trough-like ovipositor, curved slightly upward and lying beneath the tip of the abdomen. The wingtips are tinted orange in juvenile females.

Ecology: This species ranges south to near Lake Okeechobee, and north to Virginia, Kentucky, and southern Illinois, west to Missouri and Louisiana. It also occurs on the Coastal Plain north to New Jersey. The recorded Florida flight season is June 30 to December 21. The breeding habitat is not known, but various clues indicate that it might be either boggy forest trickles or sheet-flow swamp thickets.

Behavior: The Fine-lined Emerald feeds over roads or forest clearings from near the ground to the treetops, and perches on the twigs of trees. They may both perch and hunt in dense shade. Mating pairs perch on tree trunks and twigs in the treetops.

Fig. 59. Pale-sided Shadowfly, female.

SHADOWFLIES
Genus *Neurocordulia*

Shadowflies are medium sized orange to brown dragonflies which hang from twigs in dense shade by day, but become hyperactive for short periods at dawn and dusk. The thorax has a yellow dot on each side and the wings usually have a series of small brown dots along the front edges. Unlike most Emeralds, the eyes are never metallic green. This genus is found only in North America, and 3 of the 6 species occur in the Florida Peninsula.

PALE-SIDED SHADOWFLY   *Neurocordulia alabamensis*

Identification: Common but seldom seen, medium sized, 41-46 mm (1.6- 1.8 in) long.

Body brownish orange with dull waxy yellow sides on the thorax. Each wing has a row of amber dots along the front edge from base to stigma.

The Cinnamon Shadowfly is very similar, but is a little browner, the sides of the thorax are not particularly paler than the front, and no dots are present between the middle of the wings and the stigma. Baskettails have dark brown abdomens with yellow lateral stripes, and no amber wing markings (may have brown markings). The Fawn Darner and Twilight Darner are much larger, and the Fawn has 2 yellow spots on each side of the thorax.

Ecology: The Pale-sided Shadowfly ranges south to near Lake Okeechobee. It occurs in the coastal states from eastern Texas to North Carolina. The habitat is small forest streams, and the recorded Florida flight season is May 6 to August 2.

Behavior: This is one of the most elusive dragonflies, because its dusk flight period lasts only 10 to 20 minutes, commencing about 40 minutes before total darkness. They often start flying 1 or 2 m above the water, then fly lower as the light gets dimmer. Females lay eggs during a rapid crisscrossing flight over pools or under overhanging branches, making rapid taps to the water from about 8 cm above the surface.

Fig. 60. Cinnamon Shadowfly, female.

CINNAMON SHADOWFLY   *Neurocordulia virginiensis*

Identification: Northern Florida, common, medium sized, 41-49 mm (1.6-2.0 in) long.

Body pale orange-brown. Males have most of the larger wing veins pale, and appear to have pale orange wings and body when they are in flight at dusk over a river. The female appears browner in flight. A few small dark dots are placed along the front of each wing near the base. Also see Identification of the similar Pale-sided Shadowfly.

Ecology: The Cinnamon Shadowfly occurs south to Ocala, north to Virginia and Tennessee, west to Oklahoma and Louisiana. The habitat is generally rivers, especially rock-bottomed ones with riffles. The recorded Florida flight season is mostly earlier than that of the Pale-sided Shadowfly, March 18 to June 11.

Behavior: The Cinnamon Shadowfly may hunt along branches in the forest understory, in addition to feeding in the open. The dusk flight may start before sunset in shady areas, and usually lasts for the 45 to 90 minutes preceding darkness. The flight is often divided into two sections. In the first, the dragonflies fly 1-2 m above the water, wild, erratic, and wary. When 2 or 3 males meet, they whirl in an aggressive skirmish for several seconds. After a lull of a few minutes, the second flight of about 30 minutes duration continues until total darkness. The second flight is lower, about 15 cm above the water. Near dark, flight may be restricted to small areas near shore, and the insects are less wary. Mating occurs at rest in trees during the dusk flight or early in the morning.

Fig. 61. Umber Shadowfly, male.

UMBER SHADOWFLY   *Neurocordulia obsoleta*

Identification: Northern Florida, rare, medium-sized, 41-48 mm (1.6- 1.9 in) long.

The body is brown; each wing has a large black spot at the base, a small black spot at the middle front edge, and a series of dots between those spots.

The Common Baskettail may have a similar basal wing spot, but has yellow lateral stripes on the abdomen.

Ecology: The Umber Shadowfly has been found near Gainesville emerging from larvae in April at sand-bottomed lakes edged with Bald Cypress trees. The species ranges north to Maine, and west to Michigan, Illinois, and Louisiana.

Behavior: The habits of this species in Florida are not known. In the north it flies at dusk over riffles of rivers.

SKIMMERS
Family Libellulidae

Skimmers are the most common as well as the most showy dragonflies. Most species breed in still water, but a few can reproduce in running water. Many species have a conspicuous wing pattern, and some have red, white, or blue markings on the abdomen. Among other Florida dragonflies such wing patterns are found only in certain Emeralds, and such abdominal colors only in certain Darners. Many Skimmers oviposit in tandem; the only other Florida dragonfly that does this is the Common Green Darner. Skimmers can be recognized by the foot-shaped loop of veins near the base of the hindwing, complete with knee, heel, and toe (see Fig. 77). This loop helps support the base of the hindwing, and is particularly well developed in the widened wings of gliding species. Males lack flaps on abdominal segment 2 and the correlated angles at the base of the hindwing; thus the hindwing shape is similar in males and females. As in most dragonflies, the eyes are in contact on top of the head.

KING SKIMMERS
Genus *Libellula*

These are the dominant dragonflies at many still water habitats. Males of certain species are our only dragonflies with white wing markings; these are produced by white pruinescent wax on the wings. Females of all our species have lateral flaps on the margins of abdominal segment 8 which can be used as a scoop to throw drops of water containing eggs onto the bank. Presumably such eggs are safer from predators during their incubation period than they would be in the water.

The classification of this group is controversial. Some entomologists place the Corporal Skimmer in the genus *Ladona*, and some place the Common Whitetail either in the genus *Plathemis* or in *Platetrum*. Of the 22 North American species, 9 range into the Florida Peninsula.

Fig. 62. Common Whitetail, mature male.

COMMON WHITETAIL   *Libellula lydia*

Identification: Northern Florida, common, medium-sized, 38-48 mm (1.5-1.9 in) long.

    This dragonfly has a chunky biplane-like shape and rapid smooth flight. Mature males are easily recognized by the wide black band across each wing and the pruinose white abdomen. They also have a white spot at the base of the hindwing. The female looks very different from the male. She has 3 brown spots in each wing — at the base, middle, and tip. The abdomen is brown with white interrupted zig-zag lateral stripes. Juvenile males have the wings banded as in mature males, but the abdomen colored as in females.

Ecology: This species is common south to Gainesville, rare south to Ocala. It ranges throughout the U.S., and penetrates southern Canada and northern Mexico. In Florida the habitat is usually shallow sunny seepages and trickles with a soft mud bottom. However, it can breed in nearly any still water area or in the margins of slow moving streams. It is fairly tolerant of organic pollution. The recorded Florida flight season is February 9 to November 16. In most years it appears about the third week in March.

Behavior: The Common Whitetail perches on the ground, logs, or weed stems. Males mature in about 2 weeks, females in 2-3 weeks. Males defend territories about 10 m (up to 30 m) long near shore, where they threaten other males by raising their abdomens to display the white coloration. Each male can defend a territory for about 2-3 hours before being ousted by another male. They become more aggressive when crowded by neighbors; when many other males are present, each male attacks any other that tries to perch within 1.25 m. Mating takes only 3 seconds while the pair hovers. The female carries a heavy payload of about 1000 eggs, which she deposits in less than 7 minutes with rhythmic dips to the water surface. The male usually hovers above her to guard her from the attentions of other males. Females can produce a clutch of eggs every 1 or 2 days.

    This is one of the most-studied dragonflies. Additional data can be found in Campanella and Wolf (1974), Dickerson et al (1982), Jacobs (1955), Koenig and Albano (1985 and 1987), and McMillan (1984).

Fig. 63. Common Whitetail, female.

Fig. 64. Painted Skimmer, male.

PAINTED SKIMMER   *Libellula semifasciata*

Identification: Northern Florida, uncommon, medium-sized, 36-48 mm (1.4-1.9 in) long.

This species is readily identified by its wing pattern: amber at the base and tip, with brown streaks at the base, a brown spot at mid-wing, and a brown band at the stigma. The thorax is brown with 2 pale stripes on each side; the abdomen is orange with a mostly black tip. The base of the abdomen is transparent, allowing the internal air spaces to be visible in dorsal view.

Ecology: The Painted Skimmer ranges south to Orlando, and north to Maine, southern Ontario, and Wisconsin, west to Illinois, eastern Kansas, and eastern Texas. Its habitat is marshy forest ponds and sometimes streams. The recorded Florida flight season is February 27 to September 19. It is most common in the spring, with only stragglers present later in the season.

Behavior: This species is somewhat wary and usually perches on the tips of tall weeds or on twigs. Mating occurs in flight, and the male guards the female while she oviposits with quick dips to the water among emergent plants.

Fig. 65. Corporal Skimmer, mature male.

Fig. 66. Corporal Skimmer, female.

CORPORAL SKIMMER

Libellula exusta deplanata

Identification: Common, size small, 29-40 mm (1.1-1.6 in) long.

This species is identified by its small size, early spring flight season, and habit of perching on the ground, as well as by its coloration. The thorax is brown with a pair of creamy white stripes on the front (Corporal refers to these shoulder stripes). In females and juvenile males the abdomen is brown with an irregular dorsal black stripe. The front of the thorax and the abdomen become pruinose pale blue in mature males. The base of each wing has 2 brown streaks.

Some entomologists consider the New England form, which has a white abdomen in mature males, a species (*Libellula exusta*) separate from the southern *Libellula deplanata*.

Ecology: The Corporal Skimmer is found in most of the Florida Peninsula, south to Naples. It ranges north to New Brunswick and Nova Scotia, and from Virginia west to eastern Kansas and eastern Texas. The habitat is still water, or occasionally trickles or streams, but it is most common in sand-bottomed lakes or newly made borrow pits. This is an early spring species, recorded in Florida from January 4 to May 6.

Behavior: This species typically perches on the ground, low stems, or floating objects, and when the temperature is cool it commonly basks on tree trunks. Males patrol in a fast low wavering flight with some hovering. Mating occurs in flight and lasts for about 10 seconds. Then the female oviposits with rapid dips among water lilies or other vegetation while her mate guards against intruding males.

GOLDEN-WINGED SKIMMER

Libellula auripennis

Identification: Common, medium sized, 42-58 mm (1.7-2.3 in) long.

In a female or juvenile male the face and the front of the thorax are brown, each side of the thorax has 2 diffuse pale stripes, the stigma is yellow, and the abdomen is yellow with a dorsal black stripe. In a mature male the face, front of the thorax, wing veins, and abdomen become orange, while the stigma becomes red. The lower part (tibia) of the hind leg is black.

The female Purple Skimmer is identical in appearance to the female Golden-winged; these can not be separated unless they are seen mating with a male of one or the other species. Needham's Skimmer is also very similar, but the mature male is redder, with brown hind tibiae and dark posterior wing veins. Female and juvenile male Needham's have the pale sides of the thorax not striped, but with a nose-like pale extension anterior to the shoulder and above the base of the middle leg. Also the costa vein is dark from the base to the middle of the wing, whereas the whole vein is pale in the Golden- winged.

Ecology: The Golden-winged Skimmer is common throughout most of the Florida Peninsula, but appears to be rare south of Lake Okeechobee. It ranges north to Massachusetts, and west to Missouri and eastern Texas. The habitat is usually grassy ponds and lakes, but includes ditches and slow streams. The recorded Florida flight season is February 23 to October 21.

Behavior: This dragonfly forages from perches on weed stems in open fields. Males usually perch on the tips of weeds, females halfway down the stem. Its prey includes damselflies, small dragonflies, and small grasshoppers. The males at water are active and rather wary. They perch on weed tips at the waters edge, or hover and fly about 1 m over open water. Females dip to the water to oviposit as in other King Skimmers, as the male perches or hovers above on guard.

Fig. 67. Golden-winged Skimmer, mature male.

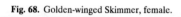

Fig. 68. Golden-winged Skimmer, female.

Fig. 69. Purple Skimmer, mature male.

PURPLE SKIMMER

Libellula jesseana

Identification: Scarce, medium-sized.

This species is identical in structure to the Golden-winged Skimmer. The females are also identical in color and can not be identified unless they are seen mating with a male Purple Skimmer. The beautiful mature male Purple Skimmer has a black face, the wings clear in the basal 1/4 but deep orange beyond, and a pruinose pale blue to dark blue body. Juvenile males have a dark brown face and body.

Ecology: This species is apparently endemic to Florida. In the Florida Peninsula it is found at certain sand-bottomed lakes on the eastern side of the peninsula south to Palm Beach. The recorded flight season is April 21 to September 12.

Behavior: Like that of the Golden-winged Skimmer, except that males defend territories in areas of sparse emergent grass, whereas the Golden-winged uses dense grass at the same lakes. Male Purple Skimmers prefer to locate territories near bushes or trees, but they are apparently not territorial at high population densities. They tend to fly higher and faster than male Golden-winged.

Fig. 70. Needham's Skimmer, mature male.

NEEDHAM'S SKIMMER
Libellula needhami

Identification: Common, medium sized.

See Identification of the very similar Golden-winged Skimmer. Needham's Skimmer was named for the American entomologist James Needham.

Ecology: Needham's Skimmer is common in Florida along the coasts and on the Keys. It also occurs inland, especially in southern Florida. Outside of Florida the species occurs in the coastal states north to Massachusetts and west to Texas, as well as in Arkansas, Mexico, the Bahamas, and Cuba. Needham's Skimmer can breed in brackish water and fertilized waters, principally marshes, lakes, ponds, and canals. Its recorded Florida flight season is February 20 to November 1.

Behavior: Like that of the Golden-winged Skimmer. They may feed during sustained flight as well as from perches. Pairs mate for about 20 seconds, perching for most of that time, and the male guards the female as she oviposits for several minutes.

Fig. 71. Great Blue Skimmer, mature male.

GREAT BLUE SKIMMER

Libellula vibrans

Identification: Common, fairly large, 49-62 mm (2.0-2.4 in) long.

This is our largest Skimmer. In juveniles the face is white, the eyes are red-brown, the front of the thorax is brown with a white median stripe, the sides of the thorax are pale gray, and the abdomen is yellow with a black dorsal stripe. The wings are marked with black, including a streak at the base, a spot at the middle, and a black tip, which in females extends to the stigma. Some individuals have a black bar along the front of the wing near the stigma, as in the Bar-winged Skimmer. In mature females the eyes become blue and the abdomen becomes brown. In mature males the eyes are blue, and the front of the thorax as well as the abdomen become pruinose pale blue. Males become pruinose first on the thorax.

Juveniles are very similar to juveniles of the Bar-winged and Slaty Skimmers. See Identification under those species.

Ecology: The Great Blue Skimmer is found south to Naples, and north to Massachusetts, west to extreme southern Ontario, Wisconsin, eastern Kansas, and eastern Texas. The habitat is swamp pools and slow forest streams. The recorded Florida flight season is March 24 to October 11.

Behavior: This is one of our tamest large dragonflies, often allowing a face-to-face inspection. It often perches in the shade, from where it takes prey such as deer flies, beetles, damselflies, or even newly emerged Slaty Skimmers. Males may begin patrolling a territory and can mate before their abdomens are fully pruinose. They are dominant to Bar-winged Skimmers. Pairs mate for about 25 seconds on a perch, after which the female oviposits, usually throwing droplets of water containing eggs on the bank. The male guards the female by hovering about 20 cm above her.

Fig. 72. Great Blue Skimmer, mature female.

Fig. 73. Great Blue Skimmer, juvenile female.

Fig. 74. Slaty Skimmer, mature male.

SLATY SKIMMER   *Libellula incesta*

Identification: Common, medium sized, 45-56 mm (1.8-2.2 in) long.

    Juveniles are similar to those of the Great Blue Skimmer, but have a brown face and a brown triangular marking on the side of the thorax at the base of the forewing. The pale pattern on the side of the thorax resembles the head of a cartoon wolf. Males and some females lack black basal wing streaks, and only a tiny spot may be present at the middle of the wing. In mature females the eyes remain red-brown, while the abdomen becomes brown or lightly pruinose. In mature males the face is black, the eyes are dark brown, and the body is pruinose black.

    Compare this species with the similar Great Blue and Bar- winged Skimmers.

Ecology: The Slaty Skimmer ranges throughout the Florida Peninsula, and north to Maine, southern Ontario, and Wisconsin, west to eastern Kansas and eastern Texas. The habitat is nearly any quiet water with a muck bottom, usually in or near forest, and including rivers. Low populations of this species may inhabit sand-bottomed lakes with forested shores. The recorded Florida flight season is March 21 to November 7.

Behavior: This species is the crow among dragonflies — black, common, and conspicuous. It perches on the tops or stems of weeds or twigs. Males are most active over water in the morning. Mating takes about 30 seconds to 1 minute including a short period of perching. Females oviposit by flipping water drops as in most King Skimmers, and may lay eggs out in open water as well as along the shore. The male guards the female with fast back-and-forth flights above her. Females with the abdomen still in the yellow juvenile coloration can lay eggs.

Fig. 75. Slaty Skimmer, female.

Fig. 76. Bar-winged Skimmer, mature male.

BAR-WINGED SKIMMER   *Libellula axilena*

Identification: Fairly common, medium sized, 48-62 mm (1.9-2.4 in) long.

    Mature males are black with pale gray-blue areas on the front of the thorax, between the wings, and abdominal segments 1 to 3. They also have a distinctive touch of white at the base of the hindwing. Each wing has small black markings, including a streak at the base, a spot at the middle, a bar or spot along the front margin in the outer half, and the tip. Females and juvenile males are almost identical to those of the Slaty Skimmer, but are usually a little larger, and although the face is dark it has contrastingly pale lateral borders. Maturing male Bar-winged Skimmers quickly aquire the white area at the base of the hindwing, then the front of the thorax becomes pruinose gray. Note that male and some female Slaty Skimmers lack black streaks at the base of the wings.

    Compare this species with the Slaty and Great Blue Skimmers.

Ecology: The Bar-winged Skimmer ranges south to Palm Beach, and to Louisiana, Arkansas, and Kentucky, and north along the east coast to New York. The habitat is swampy forest pools and ditches. The recorded Florida flight season is March 25 to October 19.

Behavior: Like that of the Slaty Skimmer. Perches from weed tips to tree tops, or sometimes flies with raised wings in sustained feeding flights. Food includes grasshoppers. Males perch over swampy pools, and mating pairs perch on a weed or bush for 30 seconds. The female oviposits as in other King Skimmers, while the male hovers above her on guard.

Fig. 77. Roseate Skimmer, mature male of Pink Form.

ROSEATE SKIMMERS
Genus *Orthemis*

This genus differs from the King Skimmers in details of the wing vein arrangement, and only one species occurs in North America.

ROSEATE SKIMMER   *Orthemis ferruginea*

Identification: Common, medium sized, 46-56 mm (1.8-2.2 in) long.

The mature male Roseate Skimmer is very striking in either of its two color forms. The pruinose Pink Form is common and has a pale blue thorax and a pink to red-violet abdomen. The Red Form is entirely bright red, but is scarce and normally found only in the Keys. A juvenile male or a female has a brown thorax with white stripes in an irregular HIII pattern on each side, and the abdomen is rusty brown. A median white stripe extends from the neck over the thorax to the base of the abdomen. The female has lateral flanges on abdominal segment 8 as in the King Skimmers.

The Red Pennant of southern Florida is smaller and has a brown thorax without pale lateral stripes. The Scarlet Skimmer is much smaller.

Ecology: The Roseate Skimmer was known in Florida only from the Keys from 1875 to 1930. Since that time it has spread throughout the Florida Peninsula, reaching northern Florida by 1949. It now ranges north to North Carolina, west to Arkansas, Kansas, and California, and south throughout Central and South America, the Bahamas, the West Indies, and in Hawaii. Its habitat is lakes, ditches, slow streams, ponds, and trickles in the open. It can breed in brackish or temporary muddy ponds, such as those formed during road or housing construction, and this is no doubt one of the reasons it has become common recently in Florida. The Roseate Skimmer flies all year in Florida.

Behavior: The behavior is generally like that of the King Skimmers. The species forages from perches on weed stems in fields on prey as large as damselflies. Males patrol territories about 10

Fig. 78. Roseate Skimmer, mature male of Red Form.

m long, and have an adult life span of at least 6 weeks. They hover often, and are fast fliers and quick dodgers. Males may patrol over water before they are fully pruinose. Mating requires only about 8- 12 seconds, and occurs entirely in flight. The male then guards the female for the 1-3 minutes in which she lays her eggs. A male often bends the tip of the abdomen downward while in pursuit of an intruding male. Where there is great competition for females, the male hovers close above her with the posterior half of his abdomen bent downward at a right angle. The female may flick water drops containing eggs onto the bank as in the King Skimmers, and she curves her abdomen downward more when ovipositing near shore.

The behavior of this species was studied by Harvey and Hubbard (1987), Novelo and Gonzalez (1984), and Young (1980).

Fig. 79. Roseate Skimmer, female.

Fig. 80. Scarlet Skimmer, mature male.

SCARLET SKIMMERS
Genus *Crocothemis*

Only one species of this genus occurs in North America, where it was accidentally introduced by man from Asia. Scarlet Skimmers are similar to Dragonlets (*Erythrodiplax*) in structure, but none of the North American Dragonlets are bright red.

SCARLET SKIMMER   *Crocothemis servilia*

Identification: Southern Florida, common, medium sized, 37-43 mm (1.5-1.7 in) long.

The beautiful mature male is entirely bright red. Females and juvenile males are pale yellow, with white shoulder stripes and white between the wings, and a black dorsal stripe on the abdomen. The female has a spout-like ovipositor under abdominal segment 9. Both sexes have a small amber spot at the base of each hindwing.

The Red Pennant is larger, with a black dorsal stripe only on abdominal segments 8 and 9. The male has a brown thorax and a swollen base on the abdomen, the female has neither shoulder stripes nor ovipositor. The Wandering Glider lacks shoulder stripes and does not perch much.

Ecology: The Scarlet Skimmer was accidentally introduced into Florida from Asia. It was first discovered near Miami in 1975. By 1986 it had spread to the Orlando area. In the Old World the species ranges from the Middle East to Asia and Australia. Its habitat is lakes, ditches, canals, slow streams, and ponds. It can breed in temporary ponds and is tolerant of some organic pollution. It has a year-round flight season, and in the tropics can have 3 generations per year.

Behavior: These dragonflies forage from low perches in fields. A male usually perches with wings cocked downward on low plants on the bank of his territory, and pairs perch in similar places for the less than 2 minutes required for mating. Males threaten each other by curling the abdomen upward to display its red color. Females deposit eggs with quick dips for about 1 minute in algae or over shallowly submerged plants.

90

Fig. 81. Scarlet Skimmer, female.

Begum et al (1985), and Higashi (1969) studied the behavior of this species.

Fig. 82. Blue-faced Meadowfly, mature male.

MEADOWFLIES
Genus *Sympetrum*

These are small to medium sized dragonflies in which the mature males usually have red markings. They require more time for mating, about half an hour, than most Skimmers. Only 2 of the 12 North American species range into the Florida Peninsula.

BLUE-FACED MEADOWFLY   *Sympetrum ambiguum*

Identification: Northern Florida, scarce, size small, 31-38 mm (1.2- 1.5 in) long.

This slender dragonfly has the upper part of the face green to blue (color disappears in dry specimens), while the lower face is white. The thorax is gray, the legs are tan, and in females and juvenile males the abdomen is brown with diffuse black bands around segments 4 to 9. The abdomen becomes mostly red in mature males. The eyes are red-brown in juveniles, aqua-gray at maturity.

Ecology: This species ranges south only to Gainesville, but occurs north to New Jersey, southernmost Ontario, and Minnesota, west into eastern Nebraska and eastern Texas. It is also found north along the east coast into Maine. The favored habitats are overflow pools in river bottomlands, and temporary semi-shaded ponds. It also inhabits marshes and permanent ponds. The recorded Florida flight season is May 3 to November 20.

Behavior: The Blue-faced Meadowfly is inconspicuous because it often perches on twig tips in forest shade, sometimes above human eye level. It often perches with the abdomen elevated 45 degrees. Mating pairs perch on the ground or on weed stems. The female drops her dry round eggs like little bombs as she slowly flies above the grass near a pond or perches above a dry pond bottom. The eggs roll through the vegetation down to moist soil where they hatch when the pond is again flooded by rain. The male hovers or perches nearby to guard the female from other males.

Fig. 83. Variegated Meadowfly, mature male.

VARIEGATED MEADOWFLY

Sympetrum corruptum

Identification: Scarce, medium sized, 32-43 mm (1.3-1.7 in) long.

This mostly gray dragonfly has a characteristic but complex pastel color pattern. The thorax has 2 white stripes on each side which are yellow at their lower ends, but in mature males the stripes fade and only the yellow spots remain. The abdomen has a black dorsal stripe on segments 8 and 9, and a chain of white lateral spots on segments 2 to 8. In females and juvenile males the face is tan, and abdominal segments 3 to 7 are each orange dorsally and posteriorly, but the face and orange abdominal markings turn to red in mature males. Abdominal segment 2 is black dorsally in females, orange to red in males. Several of the anterior wing veins are orange in both sexes.

This species is sometimes classified in the genus *Tarnetrum*.

Ecology: This species appears to migrate into Florida, including the Keys, in small numbers in the fall. It may not breed in the state, but is most numerous near the coasts. The species ranges throughout the U.S., where it is common in the west, and in southern Canada, and south to Honduras. It also occurs in Siberia. The habitat is still water and slow streams of nearly all kinds. It can breed in temporary brackish ponds, but seems most at home at sand-bottomed ponds in barren surroundings. The flight season is all year, but records in Florida are primarily from winter and spring.

Behavior: This dragonfly perches on the ground, or on weed tips or twigs, and is active from shortly after dawn to dusk. Males are somewhat wary, and fly and hover over open water or perch on sparse emergent vegetation. Their patrolling behavior often resembles that of the Common Baskettail. Mating pairs perch on twigs. Females oviposit in tandem over wide areas in open water or on algae.

Fig. 84. Band-winged Dragonlet, mature male.

DRAGONLETS
Genus *Erythrodiplax*

These are small to medium sized dragonflies, which in North America are black, blue, or brown. Some species have dark bands across the wings, some have 2 or 3 color forms of females, and females of some have projecting spout-like ovipositors. Three of the 4 North American species occur in the Florida Peninsula. The fourth species, the Black-winged Dragonlet (*Erythrodiplax funerea*) is found in the southwestern U.S.

BAND-WINGED DRAGONLET   *Erythrodiplax umbrata*

Identification: Southern Florida, common, medium sized, 38-47 mm (1.5-1.9 in) long.

Mature males are easily recognized by their all black slender body and a wide black band across the outer part of each wing. Females occur in 2 color forms. The Black Form looks like the male. The Brown Form is dull brown and much more common, with brown wing tips and tan rectangular lateral spots on the middle abdominal segments. Some specimens have an amber spot at the base of each hindwing. Juveniles of both sexes resemble the Brown Form female, but have gray lateral abdominal spots.

Three somewhat similar dragonflies differ in having a swollen abdominal base, the Four-spotted and Tawny Pennants, and the Black Pondhawk. The male Four-spotted Pennant also has black spots rather than bands in the wings, and both sexes of that species have white stigmas. The Tawny Pennant has a striped abdomen. A fourth species, the male Common Whitetail of northern Florida, has a stout abdomen bearing white markings.

Ecology: The Band-winged Dragonlet occurs in the southern Florida Peninsula, north to Lake Okeechobee, plus the Keys and Dry Tortugas. It also ranges from Texas throughout most of Central and South America, and in the Bahamas and West Indies. It sometimes strays as far north as Ohio. The habitat is ponds and marshes, especially temporary ones. The species flies all year.

94

Fig. 85. Band-winged Dragonlet, female of Brown Form. Note that the forelegs are not gripping the perch, a common posture of Skimmers in general if the breeze is not too strong.

Behavior: This dragonfly perches on the tips of stems or twigs, the females often high in trees. They often hover for a few seconds about 30 cm away from a perch before accepting it. Mature males are rather wary, and often patrol small pools surrounded by high vegetation. Pairs mate briefly in mid-air, then the female dips eggs into the water at scattered locations. The male does not guard her.

Fig. 86. Blue Dragonlet, mature male. The Antillean Dragonlet *Erythrodiplax justiniana* of the Bahamas is similar but has large black basal hindwing spots.

BLUE DRAGONLET *Erythrodiplax connata minuscula*

Identification: Common, size very small, 22-28 mm (0.9-1.1 in) long.

Mature males are pale blue, with a black face, black abdominal segments 8 to 10, and a small black spot at the base of each hindwing. Females and juvenile males are brown, the abdomen with a black dorsal stripe and black interrupted lateral stripes. During maturation, the male becomes blue from the front of the thorax backward and from abdominal segment 7 forward. The hindwing spot is at first amber, then changes to black. The female has an oblique scoop-like ovipositor under abdominal segment 9.

The Corporal Skimmer is a larger and stouter spring species that often perches on the ground. It has brown streaks rather than spots in the bases of the wings.

Ecology: The Blue Dragonlet ranges throughout the Florida Peninsula and the Keys, and north to Maryland, southern Ohio, and southern Illinois, west to eastern Oklahoma and Texas. Other subspecies are found from Arizona southward throughout Central and South America. The habitat is marshy ponds, lakes, and sometimes stream pools. The species flies all year.

Behavior: This dragonfly perches on low stems, often with the wings cocked downward and the abdomen elevated. It eats mostly tiny insects but sometimes attacks small damselflies. Males defend territories about 3 m in diameter where mating takes place either in flight or while perched. It requires about 3-15 seconds. Larger dragonflies usually prevent the males of this species from patrolling over open water. The male guards the female as she dips into open water or among emergent plants to lay her eggs. These dragonflies roost in grass near the water overnight.

Fig. 87. Blue Dragonlet, female.

Fig. 88. Seaside Dragonlet, mature male.

SEASIDE DRAGONLET

Erythrodiplax berenice

Identification: Common, size small, 28-35 mm (1.1-1.4 in) long.

Mature males are all black with a slender abdomen. Females have a pointed spout-like ovipositor under abdominal segment 9. Juveniles of both sexes have narrow black and yellow thoracic stripes, and abdominal segments 1 to 7 are orange-yellow dorsally. Males very rapidly develop a black thorax, and the yellow on the abdomen is reduced to small spots on segments 3 to 7, then those also disappear. Females become black like the males, but much more slowly and in 3 different ways. In the Male-like Form, the thorax becomes black before the abdomen, as in males. In the Unspotted Female Form, the abdomen becomes black before the thorax. In the Spotted Female Form the abdomen becomes black before the thorax and each wing has a large brown spot at the middle. The oldest females finally become gray on the thorax.

The Double-ringed Pennant of northern Florida is a spring species with a small black spot at the base of each hindwing. Other Small Pennants have black and amber spots at the bases of the hindwings. The Blue Dasher is larger with a white face. The Metallic Pennant of southern Florida has a brown thorax. The Black Pondhawk of southern Florida is larger with a swollen base on the abdomen. Only the female Black Pondhawk has a projecting ovipositor among these species.

Ecology: This is the only truly salt-water dragonfly in North America. Its habitats in Florida are salt marshes and mangrove swamps along the coasts, as well as in the Keys and Dry Tortugas. The species ranges from Nova Scotia to Venezuela on the Atlantic Coast, and on the Pacific Coast of Mexico. It also occurs in the Bahamas and Greater Antilles, and at certain saline lakes in the western U.S. It flies all year.

Behavior: The Seaside Dragonlet perches on stems or on the ground, and feeds on insects up to the size of lacewings and damselflies. Males perch near pools of water, either in sunlight or in shade, and defend about 5 m of shoreline. Pairs oviposit in tandem, usually into algae mats with 4 to 15 slow dips at each spot.

Fig. 89. Seaside Dragonlet, juvenile female of Male-like Form.

Fig. 90. Eastern Amberwing, male.

AMBERWINGS
Genus *Perithemis*

Dragonflies of this genus are readily recognized by their small size and chunky build, plus the orange wings of the male. The abdomen is spindle-shaped, tapered at both ends. Amberwings have the most complex courtships among North American dragonflies. Only 1 species occurs in eastern North America, 2 others are found in the southwestern U.S.

EASTERN AMBERWING   *Perithemis tenera*

Identification: Common, size very small, 20-25 mm (0.8-1.0 in) long.

This is the smallest dragonfly in the Florida Peninsula. Males are easily identified by their orange wings. Females have a variable wing pattern of brown spots or bands along with amber areas. The amount of brown in the wings generally increases southward in Florida, with some males developing brown spots or cross-bands. Both sexes have 2 wide pale greenish yellow stripes on each side of the brown thorax.

Ecology: This species is common throughout the Florida Peninsula, and ranges north to New Hampshire and southernmost Ontario, west to North Dakota, Colorado, Oklahoma, and New Mexico, and south into northern Mexico. The habitat is nearly any still waters, such as ponds, lakes, ditches, and slow parts of streams and rivers. It flies all year.

Behavior: This is one of our most interesting dragonflies, because it both mimics wasps and has a courtship. It perches on the tips of weeds or twigs and pulses its abdomen up and down while also waving its wings up and down, quite wasp-like. The females fly with the hindwings held mostly together vertically while the abdomen is bent upward along the rear edge of the hindwings; the hindwings and abdomen together look like the abdomen of a wasp. Males select some object that breaks the water surface, such as a stick, as a potential oviposition site, and defend a territory 3-6 m in diameter around it. When he arrives at water each day he must examine a site, undisturbed, for more than 5 minutes before accepting it; if he is disturbed by a predator he will

Fig. 91. Eastern Amberwing, female. This individual has raised the abdomen to the obelisk position on a hot day.

select another site. When a female appears, the male courts her by flying out to intercept her, leads her back to his oviposition site, and hovers over it with his abdomen upcurved. If the female accepts the situation, she signals that fact by beating her wings more slowly, and they perch to mate for about 20-30 seconds. The female then plasters her eggs just above the waterline as she hovers next to the oviposition site. She extends her hind legs and touches them and the abdomen to the oviposition material with each tap. The male hovers over her and guards her from other males. When the female is finished she usually flies high into the air and away. Females will also oviposit into pools of water on water lily leaves, and among emergent plants.

The behavior of this dragonfly was studied by Jacobs (1955), and by Hardy (1966).

Fig. 92. Blue Dasher, mature male.

BLUE DASHER
Genus *Pachydiplax*

The only species classified in this genus is described below.

BLUE DASHER   *Pachydiplax longipennis*

Identification: Abundant, small to medium sized, 26-44 mm (1.0-1.7 in) long.

Mature males are easily identified by the white face, metallic green eyes, black and yellow striped thorax, and a pale tapered abdomen which has a black tip. The hindwing has 2 black streaks within an amber spot at the base, and the outer half of the wing is often tinted brown. Females have a short blunt abdomen and no black streaks in the hindwing. In juveniles, the abdomen is black with 2 interrupted yellow stripes, and the eyes are red-brown. The abdomen and the dorsal area between the wings become pale blue during maturation, quickly in males, slowly in females. This species varies greatly in size, generally with the largest individuals present in the spring, the smallest in the fall.

The male Eastern Pondhawk has a pale blue or green thorax and a green face. The Speckled Skimmers of southern Florida have the pale spots of abdominal segment 7 larger and brighter than the more basal spots, and the abdominal spots are pale green at maturity.

Ecology: The Blue Dasher is found throughout the Florida Peninsula, the Keys, the Dry Tortugas, and in fact throughout the U.S. It also occurs in southernmost Canada, and in Mexico, Bermuda, and the Bahamas. The habitat is nearly any still water, including ponds, marshes, bays, ditches, and swamps. It flies all year.

Behavior: This dragonfly is usually seen perching with lowered wings on the tips of twigs or stems, in sunlight or in shade, and from near the ground to the treetops. On hot days individuals raise their abdomens straight up in the obelisk position which reduces the surface exposed to the sun by about 60%. However, they will obelisk even when perching in shade. They capture about 300 prey insects each day, amounting to about 10-15% of their body weight. The prey is usually tiny

Fig. 93. Blue Dasher, juvenile female.

insects, but sometimes is as large as damselflies. Some individuals of both sexes defend a favored feeding perch for up to several days. A male defends a breeding territory at the shoreline, and threatens other males with his raised blue abdomen. He sometimes establishes a different territory on the same day. Pairs mate for 20 seconds to 2 minutes either in flight or while perched. The male then guards the female, perching over her if possible, hovering over her if perching is not possible, while she deposits eggs. She hovers very close to the water surface, preferably over shallowly submerged vegetation, and repeatedly lowers just the abdomen tip to the surface. It takes her only about 35 seconds to lay 300-700 eggs, which she does approximately every other day. This species roosts in the trees at night.

Food requirements of this species were studied by Fried and May (1983), and the behavior by Johnson (1962), Robey (1975), and Sherman (1983).

Fig. 94. Eastern Pondhawk, mature male.

PONDHAWKS
Genus *Erythemis*

North American species in this genus are medium sized dragonflies colored black, blue, or green. They are voracious even by dragonfly standards, and will attack other insects as large as themselves. Unlike most Skimmers, they often perch on the ground. Three of the 4 North American species are found in the Florida Peninsula. The fourth, the Western Pondhawk (*Erythemis collocata*), is found in the west.

EASTERN PONDHAWK   *Erythemis simplicicollis*

Identification: Abundant, medium sized, 36-50 mm (1.4-2.0 in) long.

Mature males are pale blue with a green face. Females and juvenile males are grass green with large rectangular dorsal black spots on abdominal segments 4 to 6, and mostly black segments 7 to 9. Males begin turning blue first near the base of the abdomen, then on the front of the thorax. Females have a spout-like ovipositor under abdominal segment 9.

The Great Pondhawk of southern Florida is larger and has complete dark cross-bands on abdominal segments 4 to 6 instead of just dorsal spots. The Blue Dasher has a black and yellow striped thorax and a white face. The Corporal Skimmer is a smaller spring species with brown streaks in the wing bases and a brown face. Due to its habit of perching low or on the ground, the Eastern Pondhawk often acts like a Clubtail, but it is brighter green than any peninsular Florida Clubtail, and the eyes touch on top of the head (eyes separate in Clubtails).

Ecology: The Eastern Pondhawk is common throughout Florida including the Keys and Dry Tortugas. It ranges throughout the U.S. east of the Rocky Mountains, north into southern Quebec and southern Ontario, and west from Texas to Arizona. It also occurs south to Costa Rica, and in the Bahamas, Cuba, Hispaniola, and Jamaica. It flies all year, and its habitat is slowly flowing or quiet weedy waters, including slightly brackish water. The species is usually associated with algae mats, duckweed, water lilies, or other flat plants on the water surface.

104

Fig. 95. Eastern Pondhawk, mature female eating juvenile male. This is true cannibalism, rare in dragonfly adults but common in larvae.

Behavior: This is perhaps our most ferocious dragonfly, attacking horseflies, butterflies, moths, grasshoppers, damselflies, and newly emerged dragonflies even larger than themselves, such as Roseate Skimmers. They are occasionally even cannibalistic, devouring other individuals of their own species. These dragonflies hunt from the ground or low perches, and often use a person or other large animal as a beater to flush game. They are probably one of our most beneficial insects, since they destroy great numbers of agricultural pests. Males defend a territory that usually contains low floating plants. Almost maturely-colored males begin holding territories while the sides of the thorax are still green and the tip of the abdomen is still black. Males unable to obtain a territory perch near territorial males as satellite males. An individual male may switch from territory holder to satellite several times in a day. Males have unique leap-frog contests in which one male which is following another flies under and up in front of the leading male, then the new follower repeats this maneuver, and so forth up to a dozen times. After a male captures a female, mating takes about 20 seconds to 2 minutes, and is usually completed on a perch. After the pair separates, the female remains perched for 30 seconds to 2 minutes, then deposits about 400-2100 eggs, which takes 30 seconds to 5 minutes. She can lay this number of eggs every day. She often uses her ovipositor like a pick to put eggs into an algae mat by hovering low over it and swinging the straight abdomen repeatedly and rapidly downward. Guarding males hover near females with their hind legs extended posteriorly. Both sexes roost overnight in tall weeds or brush.

The behavior of this species has been studied in detail by McVey (1985 and 1987), McVey and Smittle (1984), and Waage (1986).

Fig. 96. Great Pondhawk, juvenile male.

GREAT PONDHAWK
Erythemis vesiculosa

Identification: Southern Florida, moderately common, size fairly large, 56-65 mm (2.2-2.6 in) long.

This species is bright grass green with brown bands on abdominal segments 4 to 7, and brown segments 8 to 10. The abdomen is inflated at segments 1 to 3, but is very slender beyond. Juveniles are our only dragonflies with a green stigma. This species is placed alone in the genus *Lepthemis* by some entomologists.

The Eastern Pondhawk is similar but smaller, with dorsal black spots instead of bands on abdominal segments 4 to 6, and females have a projecting ovipositor.

Ecology: The Great Pondhawk occurs north only to Fort Myers, and south into the Keys and Dry Tortugas. The species is also found from Oklahoma and Arizona south to Paraguay, and in the Bahamas and West Indies. The habitat is nearly any quiet water, including temporary ponds. It flies all year, but is scarce in Florida in the spring.

Behavior: This dragonfly hunts from the ground, low stems, or bushes, taking prey as large as butterflies and dragonflies. A male patrols with the abdomen raised 30 degrees over areas 10-20 m in diameter, hovering often. They are rather wary of people. Pairs perch during mating, and the female oviposits in several limited but separated places during a low flight over the water. She may lay eggs from near shore to well out in open water, tapping the surface every 2 seconds.

106

Fig. 97. Black Pondhawk, juvenile male.

BLACK PONDHAWK   *Erythemis plebeja*

Identification: Southern Florida, fairly common, medium sized, 41-49 mm (1.6-2.0 in) long.

    This species has a small black spot at the base of each hindwing. Mature males are all black, and the abdomen is extremely slender beyond the swollen segments 1 to 3. Females and juvenile males are dark brown, with the front of the thorax and bands across abdominal segments 4 to 7 tan. In males, the tan abdominal bands darken dorsally first, forming lateral spots before they disappear during maturation. A female has the base of the abdomen somewhat swollen, and a spout-like ovipositor under segment 9.

    The male Marl Pennant has large black basal hindwing spots and a normally shaped abdomen. Female Band-winged Dragonlets and male Slaty Skimmers do not have the abdomen swollen basally. The Metallic Pennant is much smaller. All of these dragonflies usually perch on the tips of stems or twigs, the Black Pondhawk usually perches low on the sides of stems.

Ecology: The Black Pondhawk was first discovered in Florida in 1971 at Miami, and has since spread sparingly north to Orlando. It also occurs from southern Texas south to Paraguay, and in the Greater Antilles. It flies all year near its habitat of quiet waters such as ponds, lakes, canals, and slow rivers.

Behavior: The Black Pondhawk is a wary, active species, usually seen perching on a low stem. Males return to water before their abdominal spots have faded. They establish territories and hover often as they patrol along weedy shores where the pairs perch to mate. Mating, which requires about 40 seconds, and oviposition are similar to those of the Eastern Pondhawk.

Fig. 98. Wandering Glider, male.

RAINPOOL GLIDERS
Genus *Pantala*

Both of the species in this genus are found in Florida. They are medium sized dragonflies with a streamlined tear-drop shaped body that tapers from the large round head to the tip of the pointed abdomen. Their hindwings are triangular, broad at the base, allowing them to remain aloft for hours. The sexes look alike. Both species allow the abdomen to droop on hot days to reduce the surface exposed to the sun.

WANDERING GLIDER *Pantala flavescens*

Identification: Common, medium sized, 44-51 mm (1.7-2.0 in) long.

This dragonfly is easily identified by its mostly yellow abdomen and sustained gliding flight. The abdomen tapers to the tip, the wings are long and broad, and the thorax is gray. In females and juveniles the face is yellow, but it develops a red tint in males. Males also aquire an orange tint to the dorsal abdomen, and brown wing tips.

Our other gliding Skimmers have a brown or black spot or band at the base of the hindwing, and the Spot-winged Glider has a brown mottled abdomen. Our other yellow Skimmers have less broadened wings and less tapered abdomens.

Ecology: The Wandering Glider is the only dragonfly found around the world. It occurs throughout Florida, including the Keys and Dry Tortugas, and in the rest of the U.S. except the northwest. It is also found in southeastern Canada, all countries of Central and South America, Bermuda, Bahamas, West Indies, Hawaii, and the Galapagos Islands. In the Old World it breeds on every continent except Europe. The species breeds in temporary ponds and puddles in the open, especially those with bare shores, including brackish ones. It flies all year, but is most common in late summer in Florida.

Behavior: This is perhaps the world's most evolved dragonfly. It drifts with the wind as it feeds on aerial plankton until an air mass of different temperature produces the rain pools in which it breeds. Over the ocean they must fly several days and nights because they reach ships thousands of km from land. In North America they apparently straggle north to breed and the offspring migrate south in the fall. Individuals often feed in swarms, sometimes following people, other large animals, or even slow-moving vehicles for the insects they stir up. These dragonflies eat mostly tiny insects, but sometimes take winged termites or even small dragonflies. They perch and roost vertically down among stems of low plants. Males patrol territories about 10-50 m long at a height of 2 m. Pairs mate in flight for 30 seconds to 5 minutes, then the female lays about 800 eggs either alone or in tandem by tapping the water at irregular intervals. Females sometimes mistake a shiny automobile or some other dry surface for water and lay eggs on it.

Reichholf (1973) described a migration of this species.

Fig. 99. Spot-winged Glider, female.

SPOT-WINGED GLIDER
Pantala hymenaea

Identification: Fairly common, medium sized, 43-50 mm (1.7-2.0 in) long.

The wings are long and broad, the thorax is gray, and the abdomen is mottled gray-brown and tapered to the tip. The round brown spot at the base of the hindwing is diagnostic but difficult to see when the insect is in flight. Females and juvenile males have a yellow to orange face which becomes red in mature males.

The Wandering Glider has a mostly yellow abdomen and no hindwing spot. Other gliding Skimmers have a differently shaped hindwing spot — a cross-band, a streak, or a triangle. Dancing Gliders do not have a mottled abdomen, nor is the abdomen so strongly tapered. Hyacinth and Pasture Gliders are smaller and more slender. The Variegated Meadowfly is smaller, lacks wing spots, and usually perches horizontally.

Ecology: The Spot-winged Glider occurs throughout Florida, including the Keys and Dry Tortugas, but is most common in southern Florida. It ranges throughout the U.S. and southernmost Canada, south throughout Central and South America, plus the Bahamas, Bermuda, West Indies, and Galapagos. It flies all year and breeds in temporary ponds and pools in the open, including brackish ones. Larval development of this species takes as little as 5 weeks.

Behavior: This dragonfly feeds with a powerful sustained flight from dawn to dark, often fast and erratic 2-5 m above the ground. The flight is more erratic with less hovering than that of the Wandering Glider. It perches vertically on twigs of bushes or trees. Males patrol territories which are larger and more linear than those of the male Wandering Glider. Females oviposit alone or in tandem by tapping the abdomen to the water, in slow hovering flight or in fast strafing runs, at well separated points.

DANCING GLIDERS
Genus *Tramea*

These medium sized red, brown, or black dragonflies have a streamlined tear-drop shaped body and broad hindwings as in the Rainpool Gliders, but they have a narrow to wide dark cross-band at the base of each hindwing. On hot days as a cooling mechanism they allow the abdomen to droop into the shade of the wing bands. The name Dancing Glider refers to the unusual tandem egg-laying behavior, in which the male releases the female's head, the female dips to the water, then the male grasps his partner again, to repeat these steps at another place. The female holds a mass of eggs between dips with a split plate under abdominal segment 9. The eggs attach to submerged plants with thin sticky threads. These dragonflies feed in a sustained gliding flight, occasionally perching horizontally on the tip of a stem or twig. It is strange that these dragonflies are almost never seen mating, although they are very commonly seen in tandem. All of the 7 North American species occur in the Florida Peninsula, including 2 vagrants to Florida.

Fig. 100. Black-mantled Glider, mature female.

BLACK-MANTLED GLIDER
Tramea lacerata

Identification: Fairly common, medium sized, 48-55 mm (1.9-2.2 in) long.

This species is mostly black, with a full width iridescent black band covering the basal fourth of each hindwing. Females and juvenile males have a yellow-brown face and large white dorsal spots on abdominal segments 3 to 7. In mature males the face becomes black and the abdominal spots darken, with the spot on segment 7 persisting the longest.

The Marl Pennant is smaller, and the basal spots of its hindwings extend across only 2/3 the width of the wing.

Ecology: The Black-Mantled Glider ranges throughout peninsular Florida and the U.S., as well as southern Ontario, Mexico, Hawaii, Bermuda, Bahamas, and Cuba. It breeds in quiet water, such as ponds, lakes, ditches, and slow streams and rivers. The species flies most of the year, recorded every month but February, but is scarce in winter.

Behavior: This is a migratory species which may fly in swarms. Some adults move north in the spring to breed, then their offspring fly south in the fall. Males patrol large areas, often a whole pond. Females oviposit either alone, or in tandem with the dancing movements described for the genus. Sometimes pairs in tandem will exhibit territorial-like chases, and sometimes the male does not release the female while she oviposits. The dips made by the female to the water are longer sweeps than in the Violet-masked Glider. Egg laying occurs on algae mats as well as in open water. The species roosts overnight either on bare twigs of trees or on grass close to the ground.

Fig. 101. Violet-masked Glider, mature male.

VIOLET-MASKED GLIDER
Tramea carolina

Identification: Common, medium sized, 45-53 mm (1.8-2.1 in) long.

A dark brown band covers the basal fourth of each hindwing, the thorax is brown, and most of abdominal segments 8 and 9 are black. The forehead is metallic violet in males, the basal half of the forehead is violet in females. In females and juvenile males the face and abdomen are brownish red, in mature males the face may become red and the abdomen turns bright red.

The scarce Red-Mantled Glider is extremely similar but has no violet on the forehead, the sides of abdominal segments 8 and 9 are pale, and the male abdomen is paler red. The hindwing band is a little smaller, extending over the basal fifth of the wing, and usually has a narrow lengthwise clear streak through its front part.

Ecology: The Violet-masked Glider ranges throughout Florida including the Keys, and north to Massachusetts, southernmost Ontario, and Wisconsin, west to Iowa and eastern Texas. It also occurs in Bermuda. The habitat is quiet water such as ponds, lakes, swamps, and slow streams, but it avoids muddy water. It flies all year in Florida.

Behavior: This species feeds from dawn to dusk, often in swarms, at heights of about 2-8 m. It exhibits some north-south migratory movement. Individuals usually perch horizontally on the tips of twigs or stems, but may perch vertically on very hot days. They also spend much more time in gliding rather than flapping flight on hot days. Males patrol large areas over the water, mostly in the morning. Mating pairs perch on tall weeds or in trees near the water for 8-10 minutes. Females oviposit either alone or in tandem with the dancing movements described for the genus, usually over submerged plants or among low emergent plants. They prefer to lay eggs in the morning or evening, but oviposit at mid-day in cloudy weather. Single females dip in the water almost 10 times faster than pairs in tandem (38 vs 4 dips/min), thus spending only about 3 minutes ovipositing instead of the 11 minutes required if they are in tandem.

Sherman (1983) provided some information on this species.

Fig. 102. Red-mantled Glider, mature male. The basal hindwing spots are partly hidden by the downward curve of the wing bases in this specimen.

RED-MANTLED GLIDER   *Tramea onusta*

Identification: Uncommon in southern Florida, rare in northern Florida. Medium sized.

See Identification of the extremely similar Violet-masked Glider.

Ecology: This species occurs sparingly throughout Florida, including the Keys and Dry Tortugas. It is generally scarce in the eastern U.S., but is common in the southwestern U.S., as it is apparently more at home in arid areas. It ranges into southernmost Ontario, and south to Venezuela, as well as the Bahamas, Cuba, Jamaica, and Puerto Rico. The habitat is quiet water such as ditches, lakes, sloughs, ponds, and stream backwaters, including temporary habitats. This Glider flies all year, but has not been recorded in Florida in January or February.

Behavior: The Red-mantled Glider cruises widely while feeding, and a male patrols a territory about 10 m wide and 30 m long. They often fly higher and faster than males of the Violet-masked Glider. Mating pairs perch on the tips of tall weeds or on twigs about 3 m above ground. Females oviposit either alone, or in tandem with the dancing movements described for the genus, sometimes placing the eggs on algae mats.

Fig. 103. Striped Glider, mature male.

STRIPED GLIDER

Tramea calverti

Identification: Rare vagrant, medium sized, 44-49 mm (1.7-2.0 in) long.

Our only Dancing Glider with a striped thorax. The thorax is brown with 2 wide gray stripes on each side, and each hindwing has a basal brown cross-band. Abdominal segments 1 to 7 are red, 8 to 10 are mostly black. The posterior part of the forehead is violet. Mature males have a red face. Females and juvenile males have a yellow face, whiter thoracic stripes, and the abdomen is paler or rustier red.

The Greater Hyacinth Glider is much smaller and has a full length black dorsal abdominal stripe.

Ecology: This is a tropical species inhabiting the West Indies and the area from southern Texas to Argentina. It apparently usually migrates from the West Indies through Venezuela in October, but some stray to Florida and the Carolinas, with a few as far as Iowa. It also occurs in the Galapagos Islands. The habitat is ponds and other quiet waters, including temporary and probably brackish ones. It flies all year in the tropics, but Florida records are in the fall.

Behavior: The Striped Glider cruises steadily over wide areas at a height of about 2 m while feeding. Males patrol at the same height irregularly over ponds in areas of about 20 m diameter.

Fig. 104. Striped Glider, female. Note parasitic mite attached under abdominal segment 2.

Fig. 105. Antillean Glider, mature male. A vagrant species to Florida, the Sooty Glider *Tramea binotata* appears identical except that the red markings are replaced by black at maturity.

ANTILLEAN GLIDER   *Tramea insularis*

Identification: Southern Florida, fairly common, medium sized, 41-48 mm (1.6-1.9 in) long.

The thorax is brown, the abdomen is red except that segments 8 and 9 are black dorsally (and laterally in some males), and segment 10 may be black. The hindwings each have a brown cross-band at the base. Males have a black face and metallic violet forehead; in females the face is brown and only the posterior part of the forehead is violet.

A very closely related tropical variety or species, the Sooty Glider *T. binotata*, has the body entirely black in mature males. One specimen of it, perhaps hurricane transported, was found just west of our area in the Florida Panhandle.

The Vermilion Glider is very similar to the Antillean, but the male has a red face and forehead. Females of these two species can not normally be differentiated without capture, but the female Vermilion lacks violet on the forehead. The Garnet Glider is smaller, with only a small brown or amber spot at the base of the hindwing, and terminal abdominal appendages much shorter than abdominal segments 9 + 10 (much longer than 9 + 10 in Dancing Gliders).

Ecology: The Antillean Glider occurs in the southeastern Florida Peninsula and in the Keys. It also is distributed in the Bahamas and Greater Antilles, and from Mexico to Venezuela. Its habitat is ponds, lakes, and ditches, and it flies all year.

Behavior: This species feeds with a rapid flight from low over fields to about 5 m high. Males patrol near shore, occasionally perching on the tips of emergent plants. The female oviposits alone or in tandem, but dips to the water at a faster rate when alone.

Fig. 106. Vermilion Glider, mature male.

VERMILION GLIDER
Tramea abdominalis

Identification: Southern Florida, fairly common, medium sized, 43-50 mm (1.7-2.0 in) long.

The thorax is brown and each hindwing has a dark brown basal cross band. In juveniles the forehead is brown, becoming red in males, yellow in females. The abdomen is brown in juveniles, red in matures, with a black dorsal stripe on segments 8 to 10.

See also Identification of the similar Antillean Glider, which has a black face and violet forehead in the male.

Ecology: The Vermilion Glider occurs in southeastern Florida and the Keys, Bermuda, Bahamas, West Indies, and from Mexico to Argentina. It has also been accidentally introduced to Hawaii. The habitat in Florida is usually ponds, but it has also been reported from swamps and stream pools. The species flies all year.

Behavior: This species usually feeds in sustained flights about 2 m high, but often perches on the topmost twigs of trees. Males patrolling over water have a Jekyll-and-Hyde behavior. In hot sunlight they patrol leisurely without hovering, but near dusk they fly very fast and erratically with brief periods of hovering. At small ponds males may patrol for only 1 or 2 minutes. Females oviposit either alone or in tandem using the dancing movements described under the genus. The male is said to guard a female ovipositing alone by hovering 1 m above her.

HYACINTH GLIDERS
Genus *Miathyria*

Only one species of this genus occurs in North America. Hyacinth Gliders are associated with floating water plants such as Water Hyacinths. They are similar to Dancing Gliders (*Tramea*) but are smaller and have a different arrangement of wing veins.

Fig. 107. Greater Hyacinth Glider, juvenile male.

GREATER HYACINTH GLIDER

Miathyria marcella

Identification: Common, medium sized, 33-40 mm (1.3-1.6 in) long.

This dragonfly has a brown thorax with 2 oblique white stripes on each side, a brown basal cross band in each hindwing, orange-brown wing veins, an orange-brown abdomen with a black dorsal stripe, and a brown face. In mature males the forehead is metallic violet, and the front and top (between the wings) of the thorax become violet. The hindwing cross band is wider in the female.

Dancing Gliders are larger, with the black of the abdomen restricted to segments 8 to 10, and only the Striped Glider has thoracic stripes. The Garnet Glider lacks thoracic stripes and has small hindwing spots.

Ecology: The Greater Hyacinth Glider occurs throughout the Florida Peninsula, and from Georgia to Texas and Arkansas, south to Argentina and the Greater Antilles. Larvae of this species live among the roots of floating aquatic plants, particularly Water Hyacinth and Water Lettuce. This insect was first found in Florida in 1934, after Water Hyacinth had been introduced in approximately 1890. The Greater Hyacinth Glider flies all year.

Behavior: This dragonfly is usually seen feeding leisurely in swarms containing both sexes about 2 m over open ground. Between bursts of flapping flight they sail with the wings slightly raised. They seldom perch, but occasionally do so vertically or obliquely on the sides of stems or twigs. Males patrol territories about 10 m long at the edge of low floating plants, flying at a height of about 30 cm and hovering often. A male may curl the abdomen upward, apparently to display its orange color, and may drive all other male dragonflies from its territory. Mating and oviposition are rarely seen, but mating occurs in flight, then the pair in tandem makes rapid dashes from a height of 1 or 2 m to place the eggs near the base of floating plants. Sometimes the male releases the female near plants, then hovers nearby to guard her as she oviposits. The female may also oviposit alone.

Fig. 108. Garnet Glider, mature male.

PASTURE GLIDERS
Genus *Tauriphila*

These are tropical dragonflies that barely range into the U.S. The Garnet Glider occurs in southern Florida, while the other North American species, the Aztec Glider (*Tauriphila azteca*), ranges to southern Texas. Pasture Gliders are similar to Dancing Gliders (*Tramea*) but are smaller and have shorter terminal abdominal appendages as well as a different arrangement of wing veins.

GARNET GLIDER   *Tauriphila australis*

Identification: Southern Florida, rare, medium sized, 40-44 mm (1.6- 1.7 in) long.

The thorax and face are brown, and a small brown spot occurs at the base of each hindwing. In mature males the abdomen is red with a narrow black dorsal stripe on segments 8 and 9, the forehead is metallic violet or blue, and the front of the thorax is black. Females and juvenile males have a brown abdomen. Females have a narrow but full length black dorsal abdominal stripe, and their hindwing spot is smaller than in males, often just an amber smudge. The terminal abdominal appendages of both sexes are much shorter than abdominal segments 9 + 10.

The Greater Hyacinth Glider is smaller, with white lateral thoracic stripes, and a basal hindwing cross-band instead of a spot. Dancing Gliders are larger, with basal hindwing cross-bands, more black on abdominal segments 8 and 9, and terminal abdominal appendages much longer than segments 9 + 10. The Spot-winged Glider is larger, with a gray thorax and mottled abdomen. The female Red Pennant has terminal abdominal appendages much longer than abdominal segment 10 (little longer in female Garnet), and forages from perches rather than in sustained flight. Tropical Pennants have a long slender abdomen with a wide black dorsal stripe from segments 3 to 9, instead of a short stripe or a line.

Ecology: The Garnet Glider occurs in the U.S. only in the southern half of the Florida Peninsula. It also occurs in Cuba, Hispaniola, and Puerto Rico, and from Mexico to Argentina. The

120

Fig. 109. Marl Pennant, mature male.

species seems to be associated with floating aquatic plants, like the Greater Hyacinth Glider, and was first reported from Florida in 1950. The Garnet Glider flies all year in the tropics, but has been recorded in Florida from early June to late October.

Behavior: This dragonfly cruises over large areas of open ground to feed at a height of 2 to 3 m. Males patrol territories over floating plants, hovering occasionally.

MARL PENNANTS
Genus *Macrodiplax*

Only a single species of this genus is found in North America.

MARL PENNANT   *Macrodiplax balteata*

Identification: Common, medium sized, 35-43 mm (1.4-1.7 in) long.

A large rounded black spot occurs at the base of each hindwing. A female or a juvenile male has a white face, a gray thorax with an irregular brown W on each side, abdominal segments 1 to 7 dull yellow, and segments 8 to 10 black. The mature male develops an entirely black face and body.

Small Pennants are much smaller. The Black Pondhawk has a very slender abdomen. Dancing Gliders are larger with a basal cross-band rather than a spot at the base of the hindwing. The Spot-winged Glider is also larger, with a hindwing spot near the posterior angle, not at junction of wing and body.

Ecology: The Marl Pennant usually breeds in brackish or mineralized waters, and thus is typically found at ponds and lakes near the coasts of Florida plus the Keys and Dry Tortugas. An inland type of habitat is a marl pond, where calcium carbonate deposits encrust submerged vegetation. The species ranges north to North Carolina, west to southern California, and south to Venezuela, as well as in the Bahamas, Cuba, Hispaniola, and Jamaica. It flies all year.

Fig. 110. Marl Pennant, female.

Behavior: This species feeds from perches on the tips of weeds or twigs from near the ground to the tree tops. On hot days they raise both wings and abdomens. It occasionally feeds in swarms with a sustained flight. Males are rather wary, and usually perch far from shore on emergent stems, from where they fly extensive irregular patrols at a height of 50 cm with some hovering. They may begin patrolling while they still have yellow abdominal spots. Females oviposit in tandem, either in open water or among surface weeds.

Fig. 111. Red Pennant, mature male.

TROPICAL PENNANTS
Genus *Brachymesia*

These are medium sized brown, black, or red dragonflies which perch on the tips of stems or twigs. The abdomen is swollen at segments 2 and 3, and has a partial or complete dorsal black stripe. The thorax is plain brown or black. All 3 species of the genus occur in the Florida Peninsula, though one is a vagrant.

RED PENNANT   *Brachymesia furcata*

Identification: Southern Florida, fairly common, medium sized, 38-45 mm (1.5-1.8 in) long.

Females and juvenile males are plain brown, with a small amber spot at the base of each hindwing. The abdomen is shorter and thicker than in our other Tropical Pennants, 1/5 shorter than a wing, swollen at segments 2 and 3, and with a narrow black dorsal stripe on segments 8 and 9. Some individuals have a white dorsal stripe between the wings that extends onto the base of the abdomen. In males the face and abdomen become bright red, and some females also develop a red abdomen.

The Scarlet Skimmer is smaller, with a full length black abdominal stripe, and the female is yellow with white shoulder stripes. Male Red Form Roseate Skimmers are much larger and lack amber at the base of the hindwing. Female Roseates have white lateral thoracic stripes and lateral flanges on abdominal segment 8.

Ecology: The Red Pennant is found in southeastern Florida, including the Keys, and along the U.S./Mexican border south to Argentina and Chile. It also occurs in the Bahamas and Greater Antilles. It flies all year near its habitat of ponds and lakes, including brackish ones.

Behavior: This species forages from the top twigs of bushes and trees. Males perch on projecting sticks in the water, either in sun or shade, and patrol territories about 15 m long, hovering approximately every 3 m when on patrol. Pairs mate in flight for 15 seconds, then the female dips eggs into the water near the shore while the male hovers over her on guard against other males.

Fig. 112. Four-spotted Pennant, mature male.

FOUR-SPOTTED PENNANT   *Brachymesia gravida*

Identification: Common, medium sized, 47-54 mm (1.9-2.1 in) long.

This is the only Florida dragonfly with white stigmas. A mature male has an all black face and body, and a large black spot in the outer half of each wing. A juvenile has white spots on the sides of the face, a brown thorax, and a brown abdomen with an irregular black dorsal stripe on segments 4 to 9, but lacks wing spots. A female darkens more slowly than a male, and eventually develops a black body and wing spots, but retains the pale facial spots. The abdomen of both sexes is slender, as long as a wing, and swollen at segments 2 and 3.

The rare Tawny Pennant is very similar to the juvenile Four- spotted Pennant, but has a tan face, tan stigmas, and a brownish yellow abdomen. Its wings turn brown at maturity, but lack spots. The Band-winged Dragonlet has brown stigmas, and either bands across the wings, or pale lateral spots on abdominal segments 4 to 7.

Ecology: The Four-spotted Pennant occurs on the Coastal Plain from Maryland south throughout Florida, including the Keys and Dry Tortugas, and west to central Texas. It has also been recorded in Oklahoma, Arkansas, Tennessee, and Nebraska. This species seems to prefer brackish or fertilized quiet waters, including ponds, lakes, and ditches. It flies all year in Florida, but is scarce in December and January.

Behavior: This dragonfly perches on the tips of tall weeds, on twigs up into the tree tops, and on telephone wires. They occasionally take prey as large as small dragonflies, and often feed in swarms early or late in the day. Pairs mate in flight for 5-15 seconds, then the female dips eggs into open water or masses of filamentous algae. The male may hover over the female to guard her from other males.

124

Fig. 113. Four-spotted Pennant, juvenile male.

Fig. 114. Tawny Pennant, mature male.

TAWNY PENNANT
Brachymesia herbida

Identification: Southern Florida, rare vagrant, medium sized.

See Identification of the Four-spotted Pennant.

Ecology: This species has been found in Florida only in the Keys, and in the past may have bred there. It occurs sparingly in southern Texas, but is common southward into Argentina. It also occurs in the West Indies and the Galapagos Islands. It flies all year near its habitat of ponds, lakes, marshes, and ditches, including those with brackish water.

Behavior: The Tawny Pennant perches on the tips of stems or twigs. Females oviposit with fast dips to the water at well separated intervals.

SMALL PENNANTS
Genus *Celithemis*

These small to medium sized colorful dragonflies with a rather delicate build perch on the tips of plant stems. Most species have a wing pattern, at least at the base of the hindwing. The face and body markings are yellow in juveniles, becoming red or black in mature males. Abdominal segments 8 to 10 are always black. Females usually oviposit in tandem with males. Seven of the 8 species in the genus occur in the Florida Peninsula. The other species, Martha's Pennant (*Celithemis martha*), is found in the northeastern U.S.

Fig. 115. Halloween Pennant, mature male.

HALLOWEEN PENNANT

Celithemis eponina

Identification: Common, medium sized, 30-42 mm (1.2-1.7 in) long.

This, our most butterfly-like dragonfly, is easily identified by the combination of orange and black wings with a yellow or red dorsal stripe on abdominal segments 3 to 7. Females and juvenile males have yellow body markings, most of which become pale red in mature males, including the face, wing veins, stigmas, and abdominal markings. Some females develop faintly red markings.

Other dragonflies with a similar pattern of dark wing markings have at least part of the wings clear and transparent.

Ecology: This species is common throughout Florida, including the Keys and Dry Tortugas. It ranges north to Maine, southern Ontario, and Minnesota, and west to Nebraska, Colorado, and Texas. It also occurs in Cuba and the Bahamas. This dragonfly flies all year near its habitat of ponds, lakes, and marshes.

Behavior: This species, with its orange and black Halloween coloration, forages from the tips of tall weeds in open fields. It often perches with forewings vertical, hindwings horizontal, and on hot days may raise the abdomen vertically while the wings shade the thorax. Almost all mating and egg laying take place from about 8 to 10:30 A.M. Mating pairs perch on vegetation close to shore for about 4 minutes, then oviposit in tandem with dips to the water in scattered locations, sometimes far from shore in the crests of waves.

Miller (1982) studied the reproductive behavior of this species.

Fig. 116. Banded Pennant, mature male. Photo by Curtis E. Williams.

BANDED PENNANT
Celithemis fasciata

Identification: Fairly common, size small, 28-38 mm (1.1-1.5 in) long.

This species is readily identified by its pattern of black wing spots, including black wingtips, a spot in the outer half of each wing, and a partial or complete ring occupying the basal half which encloses an amber area. Females and juvenile males have yellow face and body markings, both of which become entirely black in mature males. In females the extreme tips of the wings are often clear.

In the Calico Pennant, the basal wing marking occupies the basal fourth instead of the basal half of the wing, and males develop red abdominal spots. King Skimmers with a similar wing pattern are much larger with pale lateral stripes on the abdomen (pale dorsal spots in the Small Pennants).

Ecology: The Banded Pennant ranges south in Florida to near Lake Okeechobee, and north to Massachusetts, Ohio, and Wisconsin, west into Kansas and Texas. The habitat is ponds and lakes, especially new borrow pits and clear-water sand-bottomed lakes. The recorded Florida flight season is April 8 to October 28.

Behavior: This dragonfly usually feeds in the tree tops. Males are more active in the morning, when they perch on the tips of emergent plants at the edge of open water with the forewings elevated more than the hindwings. Mating pairs perch on weed tips. Females oviposit alone from a height of about 15 cm, or dip while in tandem from a height of about 30 cm, usually among emergent vegetation. This species prefers to roost overnight in pine trees.

Fig. 117. Calico Pennant, mature male.

CALICO PENNANT

Celithemis elisa

Identification: Northern Florida, uncommon, size small, 24-34 mm (1.0-1.3 in) long.

This dragonfly is readily recognized by its wing pattern of brown markings, including the wingtips, a round spot in the outer half of each wing, and an area occupying the basal fourth of each hindwing which usually encloses an amber spot or stripe. Females and juvenile males have yellow faces, stigmas, and dorsal abdominal spots, but these areas become bright red in mature males.

The Banded Pennant has black markings in the basal half, rather than the basal fourth, of each hindwing, and no red markings. King Skimmers with a similar wing pattern are much larger with pale lateral abdominal stripes, not dorsal spots.

Ecology: The Calico Pennant has been found south only to Gainesville, but ranges north to Nova Scotia, southern Ontario, and Minnesota, west to Iowa, eastern Kansas, and eastern Texas. The habitat is ponds and lakes with emergent plants or marshy borders. It seems to prefer newly made borrow pits, and may be extending its range southward in Florida by using these as "stepping stones." The recorded Florida flight season is April 12 to October 5.

Behavior: This species forages from perches on the tips of weeds in open fields. Males are active at water primarily in the morning. They are not territorial and perch near shore or in fields adjacent to the water. Males at the shore face away from the water, the object being to intercept females before they reach open water. Mating pairs perch on bushes or herbaceous plants for 5 minutes. Females oviposit in tandem either along the edge of vegetation or in open water for 3 minutes, then often alone for 2 more minutes, to deposit a total of 700-800 eggs.

Most of the behavior data above were extracted from Waage (1976).

Fig. 118. Amanda's Pennant, mature male.

AMANDA'S PENNANT

Celithemis amanda

Identification: Fairly common, size small, 24-31 mm (1.0-1.2 in) long.

A large amber spot containing 2 anterior black spots and a posterior black spot occupies the basal fourth of each hindwing. The sides of the thorax are nearly unmarked, with at most a dark anterior spot and narrow posterior stripe. Abdominal segment 3 and the basal half of segment 4 are pale. The female and juvenile male have a yellow face, thorax, and dorsal spots on abdominal segments 1 to 7. In mature males the face becomes brown to red, the thorax turns brown, and the abdominal spots change to pale red.

The Red-veined and Faded Pennants are quite similar, see Identification under those two species.

Ecology: Amanda's Pennant is found south to near Lake Okeechobee. It ranges on the Coastal Plain from Louisiana to North Carolina. The habitat is quiet water with a marginal zone of sparse emergent plants, especially newly made, clear-water, infertile, or semi- temporary ponds. Rarely, it also inhabits rivers. The recorded Florida flight season is May 15 to November 20.

Behavior: Like that of the Faded Pennant.

Fig. 119. Faded Pennant, mature male.

FADED PENNANT
Celithemis ornata

Identification: Common, size small, 28-35 mm (1.1-1.4 in) long.

The basal fifth of the hindwing is usually occupied by an amber spot containing 3 black stripes, but the spot may be small, have only 2 stripes, or in males may be nearly all brown. The sides of the thorax have 2 connected black stripes, like an upside-down V, abdominal segment 3 has a black lateral stripe, and the sides of segment 4 are mostly black. In females and juvenile males the face, thorax, and dorsal spots on abdominal segments 1 to 7 are yellow. In mature males the face and thorax turn brown, the abdominal spots change to dull red.

Amanda's Pennant is similar, but has the hindwing spot occupying the basal fourth of the wing and containing 2 anterior black spots and a posterior black spot or stripe. The sides of the thorax are nearly unmarked, and males have a redder face and abdominal spots, and a shorter abdomen, than the male Faded Pennant. In Amanda's Pennant, abdominal segment 3 and the basal half of segment 4 are pale. For other similar species see Identification under the Red-veined Pennant.

Ecology: The Faded Pennant, common throughout the Florida Peninsula, ranges in the Coastal Plain from eastern Texas to New Jersey. The habitat is quiet water such as ponds, lakes, ditches, and slow streams, which have emergent grass. The species flies all year.

Behavior: This dragonfly is often seen foraging from the tips of weeds or bushes in sparsely vegetated open places. Males perch on the tips of emergent plants bordering open water in marshy situations. Mating pairs perch on emergent grass. Females oviposit near vegetation while in tandem.

Fig. 120. Red-veined Pennant, mature male.

RED-VEINED PENNANT   *Celithemis bertha*

Identification: Common, size small, 26-36 mm (1.0-1.4 in) long.

Mature males have a bright red face and body markings, and the wing veins are red in the basal fourth as well as along the front of the wings. There is usually a very small amber or black spot at the base of each hindwing, but some, especially southern Florida males, may have an amber spot containing 2 dark stripes which covers the basal fifth of each hindwing. Juvenile males have the face and body markings yellow. The sides of the thorax are yellow with a square black anterior spot and a posterior stripe, and these markings are not usually joined. The sides of abdominal segment 3 and a lateral stripe on segment 4 are yellow. Females are similar to juvenile males, and their abdominal markings become red, but face and wing veins remain yellow.

The Faded Pennant is very similar but has the lateral thoracic black stripes connected, the sides of abdominal segment 4 mostly black, and usually large basal hindwing spots. Mature males lack red wing veins, have a brown face, and have dull red abdominal spots. Amanda's Pennant has a basal amber hindwing spot occupying the basal fourth of each wing which contains 2 black anterior spots and a posterior spot. Also the sides of the thorax are nearly unmarked. The female Marl Pennant is larger, with a white face, and with abdominal segments 4-7 mostly yellow instead of mostly black. The female Seaside Dragonlet has the thorax either all black or has many narrow black stripes on it, and the face is mostly black.

Ecology: The Red-veined Pennant is found south to Fort Myers. It ranges in the Coastal Plain from Louisiana to North Carolina. The habitat is lakes, ponds, and rarely, spring-fed rivers. They prefer infertile clear-water lakes or newly constructed borrow pits with a fringe of sparse emergent grass. The recorded Florida flight season is April 3 to December 20.

Behavior: This species forages from the tips of plants, from weeds to trees. Males perch on the tips of emergent grass furthest from shore, and mating pairs also perch there. Females oviposit in tandem, either in open water or among emergent vegetation. These dragonflies seem to prefer pine trees as overnight roosting sites.

Fig. 121. Red-veined Pennant, mature female.

Fig. 122. Double-ringed Pennant, almost mature male.

DOUBLE-RINGED PENNANT   *Celithemis verna*

Identification: Northern Florida, scarce, size small, 29-35 mm (1.1- 1.4 in) long.

Unlike other Small Pennants, abdominal segments 5 to 7 lack pale dorsal spots, even in juveniles. Each hindwing has a small black basal spot. Females and juvenile males have yellow faces and yellow rings around abdominal segments 3 and 4. The entire face and body become smoky black in mature males.

The male Seaside Dragonlet lacks a black basal hindwing spot. The male Marl Pennant is larger, with a larger basal hindwing spot. The male Slaty Skimmer is much larger and lacks basal hindwing spots. The Black Pondhawk of southern Florida is also much larger, and has the abdomen bulging at the base but very thin beyond.

Ecology: The Double-ringed Pennant has been found south in Florida only to Gainesville, but ranges north to New Jersey, Maryland, Kentucky, and Illinois, west into eastern Oklahoma and eastern Texas. The habitat is ponds, lakes, and rarely ditches and streams, with sparse emergent plants or a marginal zone of grassy plants. It apparently does not compete well with other dragonflies, and so is usually found at newly created or infertile waters. It flies in the spring, recorded in April in Florida.

Behavior: Males perch on the tips of emergent plants, usually on those furthest from shore but closest to a forested bank, and patrol areas about 7 m in diameter. Males patrol smaller areas and are less wary than male Faded Pennants. Mated pairs perch on the tips of emergent grass. Females oviposit alone or in tandem among emergent vegetation.

134

Fig. 123. Double-ringed Pennant, juvenile male.

Fig. 124. Metallic Pennant, male.

METALLIC PENNANTS
Genus *Idiataphe*

Only one species of this genus occurs in North America. Metallic Pennants are small and slender metallic black or brown dragonflies that resemble Emeralds. Unlike Emeralds, they perch horizontally on stem tips instead of vertically.

METALLIC PENNANT   *Idiataphe cubensis*

Identification: Southern Florida, common, size small, 33-38 mm (1.3-1.5 in) long.

This slender dragonfly is metallic black with the face, sides of the thorax, and lateral abdominal stripes bronzy brown. The lateral abdominal stripes extend from segment 1 to 5 in males, 1 to 9 in females. The hindwing has a small dark amber basal spot.

The male Seaside Dragonlet is smaller and entirely black. Tawny and female Four-spotted Pennants are larger, with the abdomen mostly brown instead of mostly black, and the Four-spotted has white stigmas (brown in Metallic Pennant). The Marl Pennant has a large black spot at the base of each hindwing, and the male is all black. The male Black Pondhawk is larger and has a very slender abdomen beyond its swollen base. Baskettails have full length yellow lateral abdominal stripes on a brown abdomen, and a paler and hairier thorax.

Ecology: The Metallic Pennant occurs in the U.S. only in Florida north to Lake Okeechobee, but ranges from Mexico to Honduras, and in the Bahamas and Greater Antilles. The habitat is fresh or brackish ponds and lakes, and it flies all year.

Behavior: This species forages from the topmost twigs of trees and from tall weeds, or sometimes flies high in feeding swarms. Males perch on the tips of emergent grasses, usually well out from shore, from where they make lengthy, low, and erratic patrol flights with occasional hovering. They patrol over water or sparse vegetation from near shore to well out over open water. Mating occurs in flight and lasts 20 seconds. Females oviposit with fast dips to the water, either alone or in tandem, among emergent plants or near the shore.

136

Fig. 125. Three-striped Skimmer, mature male.

SPECKLED SKIMMERS
Genus *Micrathyria*

These small tropical dragonflies are mostly black with pale green markings, including a striped thorax and spotted abdomen. Abdominal segment 10 is very short, so that the large pale spot on segment 7 superficially seems to be on segment 8. Two of the 3 North American species are found in the Florida Peninsula. The third, the Thornbush Skimmer (*Micrathyria hageni*), occurs in Texas.

THREE-STRIPED SKIMMER   *Micrathyria didyma*

Identification: Southern Florida, uncommon, size small, 32-39 mm (1.3-1.5 in) long.

The thorax is pale green with 3 black stripes on each side, the abdomen is black with 2 rows of pale green spots or streaks on segments 2 to 7 with the trapezoidal spots on segment 7 the largest. The face is white. Mature males have metallic blue-green eyes, a metallic green forehead, and a pale blue area between the wings. Females have the eyes dark metallic red dorsally, metallic green ventrally, and the forehead is brown. In juveniles the eyes are red-brown dorsally, gray ventrally, and the body markings are pale yellow.

Juvenile Blue Dashers have yellow spots on abdominal segment 8, and the spots of segment 7 are streaks rather than trapezoids. The Spot-tailed Skimmer is smaller, with a WII pattern on the sides of the thorax. Female Seaside Dragonlets have a projecting ovipositor.

Ecology: The Three-striped Skimmer was first found in the Miami area in 1985, and has not yet spread further. It is also found in the Bahamas and West Indies, and from northern Mexico to Ecuador. Its habitat is shady ponds and canals, and the species flies all year.

Behavior: This dragonfly feeds in forest clearings, where it perches with wings lowered on stem tips or twigs, often well up in the trees. Males perch on twigs over the water in the shade, and are thus rather inconspicuous.

Fig. 126. Spot-tailed Skimmer, mature male.

SPOT-TAILED SKIMMER   *Micrathyria aequalis*

Identification: Southern Florida, uncommon, size small, 26-34 mm (1.0-1.3 in) long.

The female and juvenile male have a dull yellow-green thorax with an irregular brown WII pattern on the sides. Their abdomens are brown with 2 wide interrupted pale stripes on segments 1 to 7 or 1 to 8. The face is white and the eyes are pale gray. Mature males develop bright green eyes, and a gray body with large triangular whitish green spots on abdominal segment 7. Females may become dusty gray with age, and some have brown wing tips.

Juvenile Blue Dashers and the Three-striped Skimmer have 3 straight black stripes on each side of the thorax. The female Seaside Dragonlet has a projecting ovipositor.

Ecology: The Spot-tailed Skimmer was discovered in the Miami area in 1985 and has not yet spread further. The species occurs from southern Texas to Ecuador, and in the West Indies. The habitat is ponds, lakes, and sloughs, including temporary ones. It flies all year.

Behavior: This dragonfly forages from perches on the twigs of bushes or trees, the females often back among the branches. Males at water perch on sunny or sometimes shady twigs and stems from low over the water to 2 m above it. They may hover over water for 30 seconds or so at a time and are active primarily from mid-morning to mid- afternoon. On hot days they raise the abdomen to the vertical obelisk position. The female perches on a floating leaf and curls her abdomen beneath it to lay a patch of eggs on its underside.

May (1980) studied this species.

Fig. 127. Spot-tailed Skimmer, female.

CHECKLIST OF THE DRAGONFLIES OF THE FLORIDA PENINSULA

Note on the Scientific Names: The names listed below are in alphabetical order by scientific name within each family. The name of the person who first described the species is appended onto the scientific name. A describer's name within parentheses means that he/she described the species in some other genus, then it was decided later that the species should be classified in the genus listed. The year in which the species was described is given, at no extra charge, for those who may be interested. The scientific names of animals officially became established beginning with the work of Linnaeus in 1758.

The following list includes 86 species, plus 4 vagrant species.

PETALTAILS — Petaluridae

Gray Petaltail — *Tachopteryx*
- ☐ 1. Gray Petaltail — *T. thoreyi* (Hagen,1858)

DARNERS — Aeshnidae

Green Darners — *Anax*
- ☐ 1. Common Green Darner — *A. junius* (Drury,1770)
- ☐ 2. Comet Darner — *A. longipes* Hagen,1861

Spotted Darners — *Boyeria*
- ☐ 3. Fawn Darner — *B. vinosa* (Say,1839)

Pilot Darners — *Coryphaeschna*
- ☐ 4. Blue-faced Darner — *C. adnexa* (Hagen,1861)
- ☐ 5. Regal Darner — *C. ingens* (Rambur,1842)
- ☐ 6. Mangrove Darner — *C. viriditas* Calvert,1952

Swamp Darner — *Epiaeschna*
- ☐ 7. Swamp Darner — *E. heros* (Fabricius,1798)

Pygmy Darners — *Gomphaeschna*
- ☐ 8. Taper-tailed Darner — *G. antilope* (Hagen,1874)
- ☐ 9. Harlequin Darner — *G. furcillata* (Say,1839)

Two-spined Darners — *Gynacantha*
- ☐ 10. Twilight Darner — *G. nervosa* Rambur,1842

Cyrano Darner — *Nasiaeschna*
- ☐ 11. Cyrano Darner — *N. pentacantha* (Rambur,1842)

Three-spined Darners — *Triacanthagyna*
- ☐ 12. Phantom Darner — *T. trifida* (Rambur,1842)

CLUBTAILS — Gomphidae

Forceptails — *Aphylla*
- ☐ 1. Two-striped Forceptail — *A. williamsoni* (Gloyd,1936)

Pond Clubtails — *Arigomphus*
- [ ] 2. Gray-green Clubtail — *A. pallidus* (Rambur,1842)

Spinylegs — *Dromogomphus*
- [ ] 3. Southeastern Spinyleg — *D. armatus* Selys,1854
- [ ] 4. Black-shouldered Spinyleg — *D. spinosus* Selys,1854

Common Clubtails — *Gomphus*
- [ ] 5. Blackwater Clubtail — *G.* (*Gomphurus*) *dilatatus* Rambur,1842
- [ ] 6. Clearlake Clubtail — *G.* (*Phanogomphus*) *australis* (Needham,1897)
- [ ] 7. Sandhill Clubtail — *G.* (*P.*) *cavillaris cavillaris* Needham,1902
- [ ] 8. Cypress Clubtail — *G.* (*P.*) *minutus* Rambur,1842

Dragonhunters — *Hagenius*
- [ ] 9. Dragonhunter — *H. brevistylus* Selys,1854

Sanddragons — *Progomphus*
- [ ] 10. Tawny Sanddragon — *P. alachuensis* Byers,1939
- [ ] 11. Common Sanddragon — *P. obscurus* (Rambur,1842)

Hanging Clubtails — *Stylurus*
- [ ] 12. Shining Clubtail — *S. ivae* Williamson,1932
- [ ] 13. Russet-tipped Clubtail — *S. plagiatus* (Selys,1854)

SPIKETAILS — Cordulegastridae

Spiketails — *Cordulegaster*
- [ ] 1. Twin-spotted Spiketail — *C. maculata* Selys,1854
- [ ] 2. Arrowhead Spiketail — *C. obliqua* (Say,1839)
- [ ] 3. Say's Spiketail — *C. sayi* Selys,1854

CRUISERS — Macromiidae

Brown Cruisers — *Didymops*
- [ ] 1. Maidencane Cruiser — *D. floridensis* Davis,1921
- [ ] 2. Stream Cruiser — *D. transversa* (Say,1839)

River Cruisers — *Macromia*
- [ ] 3. Georgia River Cruiser — *M. georgina* (Selys,1878)
- [ ] 4. Royal River Cruiser — *M. taeniolata* Rambur,1842

EMERALDS — Corduliidae

Baskettails — *Epitheca*
- [ ] 1. Stripe-winged Baskettail — *E. costalis* (Selys,1871)
- [ ] 2. Common Baskettail — *E. cynosura* (Say,1839)
- [ ] 3. Prince Baskettail — *E. princeps* Hagen,1861
- [ ] 4. Sepia Baskettail — *E. sepia* (Gloyd,1933)
- [ ] 5. Florida Baskettail — *E. stella* Williamson in Muttkowski,1911

Shadowflies — *Neurocordulia*
- [ ] 6. Pale-sided Shadowfly — *N. alabamensis* Hodges in Needham and Westfall,1955
- [ ] 7. Umber Shadowfly — *N. obsoleta* (Say,1839)

☐ 8. Cinnamon Shadowfly — *N. virginiensis* Davis,1927

Striped Emeralds — *Somatochlora*
☐ 9. Fine-lined Emerald — *S. filosa* (Hagen,1861)
☐ 10. Mocha Emerald — *S. linearis* (Hagen,1861)

SKIMMERS — Libellulidae

Tropical Pennants — *Brachymesia*
☐ 1. Red Pennant — *B. furcata* (Hagen,1861)
☐ 2. Four-spotted Pennant — *B. gravida* (Calvert,1890)

Small Pennants — *Celithemis*
☐ 3. Amanda's Pennant — *C. amanda* (Hagen,1861)
☐ 4. Red-veined Pennant — *C. bertha* Williamson,1922
☐ 5. Calico Pennant — *C. elisa* (Hagen,1861)
☐ 6. Halloween Pennant — *C. eponina* (Drury,1773)
☐ 7. Banded Pennant — *C. fasciata* Kirby,1889
☐ 8. Faded Pennant — *C. ornata* (Rambur,1842)
☐ 9. Double-ringed Pennant — *C. verna* Pritchard,1935

Scarlet Skimmers — *Crocothemis*
☐ 10. Scarlet Skimmer — *C. servilia* Drury,1773

Pondhawks — *Erythemis*
☐ 11. Black Pondhawk — *E. plebeja* (Burmeister,1839)
☐ 12. Eastern Pondhawk — *E. simplicicollis* (Say,1839)
☐ 13. Great Pondhawk — *E. vesiculosa* (Fabricius,1775)

Dragonlets — *Erythrodiplax*
☐ 14. Seaside Dragonlet — *E. berenice* (Drury,1770)
☐ 15. Blue Dragonlet — *E. connata minuscula* (Rambur,1842)
☐ 16. Band-winged Dragonlet — *E. umbrata* (Linnaeus,1758)

Metallic Pennants — *Idiataphe*
☐ 17. Metallic Pennant — *I. cubensis* (Scudder,1866)

King Skimmers — *Libellula*
☐ 18. Golden-winged Skimmer — *L. auripennis* Burmeister,1839
☐ 19. Bar-winged Skimmer — *L. axilena* Westwood,1837
☐ 20. Corporal Skimmer — *L. exusta deplanata* (Rambur,1842)
☐ 21. Slaty Skimmer — *L. incesta* Hagen,1861
☐ 22. Purple Skimmer — *L. jesseana* Williamson,1922
☐ 23. Common Whitetail — *L. lydia* Drury,1770
☐ 24. Needham's Skimmer — *L. needhami* Westfall,1943
☐ 25. Painted Skimmer — *L. semifasciata* Burmeister,1839
☐ 26. Great Blue Skimmer — *L. vibrans* Fabricius,1793

Marl Pennants — *Macrodiplax*
☐ 27. Marl Pennant — *M. balteata* (Hagen,1861)

Hyacinth Gliders — *Miathyria*
☐ 28. Greater Hyacinth Glider — *M. marcella* (Selys in Sagra,1856)

Speckled Skimmers—*Micrathyria*
- ☐ 29. Spot-tailed Skimmer—*M. aequalis* (Hagen,1861)
- ☐ 30. Three-striped Skimmer—*M. didyma* (Selys in Sagra,1856)

Roseate Skimmers—*Orthemis*
- ☐ 31. Roseate Skimmer—*O. ferruginea* (Fabricius,1775)

Blue Dasher—*Pachydiplax*
- ☐ 32. Blue Dasher—*P. longipennis* (Burmeister,1839)

Rainpool Gliders—*Pantala*
- ☐ 33. Wandering Glider—*P. flavescens* (Fabricius,1798)
- ☐ 34. Spot-winged Glider—*P. hymenaea* (Say,1839)

Amberwings—*Perithemis*
- ☐ 35. Eastern Amberwing—*P. tenera* (Say,1839)

Meadowflies—*Sympetrum*
- ☐ 36. Blue-faced Meadowfly—*S. ambiguum* (Rambur,1842)
- ☐ 37. Variegated Meadowfly—*S. corruptum* (Hagen,1861)

Pasture Gliders—*Tauriphila*
- ☐ 38. Garnet Glider—*T. australis* (Hagen,1867)

Dancing Gliders—*Tramea*
- ☐ 39. Vermilion Glider—*T. abdominalis* (Rambur,1842)
- ☐ 40. Violet-masked Glider—*T. carolina* (Linnaeus,1763)
- ☐ 41. Antillean Glider—*T. insularis* Hagen,1861
- ☐ 42. Black-mantled Glider—*T. lacerata* Hagen,1861
- ☐ 43. Red-mantled Glider—*T. onusta* Hagen,1861

VAGRANTS TO FLORIDA

- ☐ 1. Ringed Darner—*Anax amazili* (Burmeister,1839)
- ☐ 2. Tawny Pennant—*Brachymesia herbida* (Gundlach,1889)
- ☐ 3. Sooty Glider—*Tramea binotata* (Rambur,1842)
- ☐ 4. Striped Glider—*T. calverti* Muttkowski,1910

CHECKLIST OF THE DRAGONFLIES OF THE BERMUDA ISLANDS

Only 7 dragonfly species have been reliably recorded from the Bermuda Islands, and all are also found in the Florida Peninsula. Only a few ponds and marshes which serve as dragonfly habitats occur on the Bermuda Islands. Bermuda lies 930 km (558 miles) southeast of Cape Hatteras, North Carolina, at the latitude of Savannah, Georgia, but winters in Bermuda are moderated by the warm Gulf Stream.

DARNERS — Aeshnidae
☐ 1. Common Green Darner —*Anax junius*

SKIMMERS — Libellulidae
☐ 1. Blue Dasher —*Pachydiplax longipennis*
☐ 2. Wandering Glider —*Pantala flavescens*
☐ 3. Spot-winged Glider —*P. hymenaea*
☐ 4. Vermilion Glider —*Tramea abdominalis*
☐ 5. Violet-masked Glider —*T. carolina*
☐ 6. Black-mantled Glider —*T. lacerata*

CHECKLIST OF THE DRAGONFLIES OF THE BAHAMA ISLANDS

The Turks and Caicos Islands, although they have a different government than the Bahamas, are faunistically like the Bahamas, and are considered here along with the Bahamas.

Twenty-seven species of dragonflies have been found in the Bahamas, but none are endemic, and all but 4 species also occur in the Florida Peninsula. Several species might be only vagrants to the Bahamas, and possibly other species might invade the Bahamas from Florida or Cuba. Probably most dragonflies in the Bahamas fly all year.

There are no fresh water streams in the Bahamas. Dragonfly habitats there occur primarily on the larger islands, and consist of ponds, rock pits, and marshes. Many Bahamian surface waters are too brackish for all but a few dragonfly species.

This list was compiled from data in Dunkle (1985), Paulson (1966), and Westfall (1960).

DARNERS — Aeshnidae
☐ 1. Blue-waisted Darner —*Anax concolor* Brauer,1865
    This species is almost identical to the Comet Darner, except that the abdomen is not red. Thus this is the only large Bahamian dragonfly with an all green thorax and abdominal segments 3-10 dark brown with small pale spots. The base of abdominal segment 3 is blue in the male, white in the female. The eyes are blue at maturity. The ecology and behavior are like the Comet Darner. The species also occurs in the Greater Antilles, and from southern Mexico to Argentina.
☐ 2. Common Green Darner —*A. junius*
☐ 3. Regal Darner —*Coryphaeschna ingens*

144

Fig. 128. Blue-waisted Darner, mature male. Photo by Dennis R. Paulson.

Fig. 129. Red Setwing, mature male. Photo by Rosser W. Garrison.

☐ 4. Swamp Darner — *Epiaeschna heros*

☐ 5. Cuban Darner — *Gynacantha ereagris* Gundlach,1888

This species is very similar to the Twilight Darner, but is a little smaller (body length 62-65 mm or 2.4-2.6 in), with clear instead of brown-tinted wings (see Fig. 21). The female abdomen is constricted in dorsal view at segment 3, unlike that of the female Twilight Darner. The Cuban Darner has less than 18 crossveins between nodus and stigma in the front wing, the Twilight Darner has more than 18. The recorded flight season is July to late November. The ecology and behavior are like those of the Twilight Darner. The species also occurs in Cuba.

☐ 6. Twilight Darner — *G. nervosa*

☐ 7. Phantom Darner — *Triacanthagyna trifida*

SKIMMERS — Libellulidae

☐ 1. Red Pennant — *Brachymesia furcata*

☐ 2. Halloween Pennant — *Celithemis eponina*

☐ 3. Red Setwing — *Dythemis rufinervis* (Burmeister,1839)

This slender medium sized dragonfly has a body length of 34-40 mm (1.3-1.6 in). Its color pattern is unique, as it is the only Bahamian dragonfly with a red abdomen and a black-and-yellow striped thorax. The hindwing has a large amber basal spot. The male has a red face, the female has a yellow face and a browner body. The habitat of this species is normally rivers, streams, and lakes; thus it may be only a vagrant to the Bahamas. It perches alertly on the tips of twigs or grass. Males fly low and fast along the shore, and guard the females as they oviposit in masses of algae. The species is also found in the Greater Antilles.

☐ 4. Eastern Pondhawk — *Erythemis simplicicollis*

☐ 5. Great Pondhawk — *E. vesiculosa*

☐ 6. Seaside Dragonlet — *Erythrodiplax berenice*

☐ 7. Antillean Dragonlet — *E. justiniana* (Selys in Sagra,1857)

This dragonfly is almost identical to the Blue Dragonlet, except that mature males develop a large black basal hindwing spot (see Figs. 86 and 87). The ecology and behavior are similar to those of the Blue Dragonlet. The species also occurs in the Greater Antilles.

☐ 8. Band-winged Dragonlet — *E. umbrata*

☐ 9. Metallic Pennant — *Idiataphe cubensis*

☐ 10. Needham's Skimmer — *Libellula needhami*

☐ 11. Marl Pennant — *Macrodiplax balteata*

☐ 12. Three-striped Skimmer — *Micrathyria didyma*

☐ 13. Roseate Skimmer — *Orthemis ferruginea*

☐ 14. Blue Dasher — *Pachydiplax longipennis*

☐ 15. Wandering Glider — *Pantala flavescens*

☐ 16. Spot-winged Glider — *P. hymenaea*

☐ 17. Vermilion Glider — *Tramea abdominalis*

☐ 18. Antillean Glider — *T. insularis*

☐ 19. Black-mantled Glider — *T. lacerata*

☐ 20. Red-mantled Glider — *T. onusta*

BIBLIOGRAPHY
AND FURTHER READING

Corbet (1963 and 1980) gave a good discussion of general dragonfly biology. Books on North American dragonflies include Cannings and Stuart (1977), Needham and Westfall (1955), Walker (1958), and Walker and Corbet (1975).

Andrew, C.G. 1966. Sexual recognition in adult *Erythemis simplicicollis* (Odonata:Anisoptera). Ohio J. Sci. 66(6):613- 617.

Begum, A., M.A. Bashar, and M. Nasiruddin. 1985. Studies on the life history of *Crocothemis servilia* Drury (Anisoptera:Libellulidae). Dhaka Univ. Studies, B 33(1):137- 143.

Bick, G.H. 1983. Odonata at risk in conterminous United States and Canada. Odonatologica 12(3):209-226.

Byers, C.F. 1930. A contribution to the knowledge of Florida Odonata. Univ. Florida Biol. Sci. Series 1(1):1-327.

Campanella, P.J., and L.L. Wolf. 1974. Temporal leks as a mating system in a temperate zone dragonfly (Odonata:Anisoptera) I. *Plathemis lydia* (Drury). Behaviour 51:49-85. [Common Whitetail, *Libellula lydia*]

Cannings, R.A., and K.M.Stuart. 1977. The dragonflies of British Columbia. B.C. Prov. Museum Handbook 35, 254 pp.

Carle, F.L. 1979. Environmental monitoring potential of the Odonata, with a list of rare and endangered Anisoptera of Virginia, United States. Odonatologica 8(4):319-323.

Corbet, P.S. 1963. A biology of dragonflies. Quadrangle Books, Chicago. 247 pp.

Corbet, P.S. 1980. Biology of Odonata. Annual Review Entomol. 25:189- 217.

Dickerson, J.E.,Jr., J.V. Robinson, J.T. Gilley, and J.D. Wagner. 1982. Intermale aggression distance of *Plathemis lydia* (Drury) (Odonata:Libellulidae). SW Naturalist 27:457-458. [Common Whitetail, *Libellula lydia*]

Dunkle, S.W. 1979. Ocular mating marks in female nearctic Aeshnidae (Anisoptera). Odonatologica 8(2):123-127.

Dunkle, S.W. 1981. The ecology and behavior of *Tachopteryx thoreyi* (Hagen) (Anisoptera:Petaluridae). Odonatologica 10(3):189-199.

Dunkle, S.W. 1985. New records of Bahamian Odonata. Notulae Odonatologicae 2(6):99-100.

Dunkle, S.W., and M.J. Westfall,Jr. 1982. Odonata, pp. 32-45 *in* R. Franz, Ed., Rare and Endangered Biota of Florida Vol. 6. Univ. Florida Press. 131 pp.

Fried, C.S., and M.L. May. 1983. Energy expenditure and food intake of territorial male *Pachydiplax longipennis* (Odonata:Libellulidae). Ecol. Entomol. 8:283-292.

Hardy, H.T.,Jr. 1966. The effect of sunlight and temperature on the posture of *Perithemis tenera* (Odonata). Proc. Oklahoma Acad. Sci. 46:41-45.

Harvey, I.F., and S.F. Hubbard. 1987. Observations on the reproductive behaviour of *Orthemis ferruginea* (Fabricius) (Anisoptera:Libellulidae). Odonatologica 16(1):1-8.

Higashi, K. 1969. Territoriality and dispersal in the population of dragonfly *Crocothemis servilia* Drury (Odonata:Anisoptera). Mem. Fac. Sci. Kyushu Univ., Ser. E. (Biol) 5(2):95-113.

Jacobs, M.E. 1955. Studies on territorialism and sexual selection in dragonflies. Ecology 36(4):566-586. [Common Whitetail *Libellula lydia*, and Eastern Amberwing *Perithemis tenera*]

Johnson, C. 1962. A study of territoriality and breeding behavior in *Pachydiplax longipennis* Burmeister (Odonata:Libellulidae). SW Nat. 7(3-4):191-197.

Koenig, W.D., and S.S. Albano. 1985. Patterns of territoriality and mating success in the white-tailed skimmer *Plathemis lydia* (Odonata:Anisoptera). Amer. Midland Nat. 114:1-12.[Common Whitetail, *Libellula lydia*]

Koenig, W.D., and S.S. Albano. 1987. Breeding site fidelity in *Plathemis lydia* Drury (Anisoptera:Libellulidae). Odonatologica 16(3):249-259.

Koenig, W.D., and S.S. Albano. 1987. Lifetime reproductive success, selection, and the opportunity for selection in the white- tailed skimmer *Plathemis lydia* (Odonata:Libellulidae). Evolution 41(1):22-36.

Kormondy, E.J. 1959. The systematics of *Tetragoneuria*, based on ecological, life history, and morphological evidence (Odonata:Corduliidae). Misc. Pub. Mus. Zool. Univ. Michigan 107:1-79. [Common Baskettail, *Epitheca cynosura*]

May, M.L. 1980. Temporal activity patterns of *Micrathyria* in Central America (Anisoptera:Libellulidae). Odonatologica 9(1):57-74. [Spot-tailed Skimmer, *Micrathyria aequalis*]

McMillan, V. 1984. Dragonfly monopoly. Nat. Hist. 93:32-39. [Common Whitetail, *Libellula lydia*]

McVey, M.E. 1985. Rates of color maturation in relation to age, diet, and temperature in male *Erythemis simplicicollis* (Say) (Anisoptera:Libellulidae). Odonatologica 14(2):101-114.

McVey M.E. 1987. The opportunity for sexual selection in a territorial dragonfly *Erythemis simplicicollis*, *in* T.H. Clutton-Brock, Ed., Reproductive Success. Univ. Chicago Press.

McVey, M.E., and B.J. Smittle. 1984. Sperm precedence in the dragonfly *Erythemis simplicicollis*. J. Insect Physiol. 30(8):619-628.

Miller, P.L. 1982. Observations of the reproductive behaviour of *Celithemis eponina* Drury (Libellulidae,Odonata) in Florida. Ent. Mon. Mag. 117:209-212.

Needham, J.G., and H.B. Heywood. 1929. A handbook of the dragonflies of North America. Charles C. Thomas, Springfield, Ill. 378 pp.

Needham, J.G., and M.J. Westfall,Jr. 1955. A manual of the dragonflies of North America (Anisoptera). Univ. California Press, Berkeley. 615 pp.

Novelo, R., and Gonzalez, E. 1984. Reproductive behavior in *Orthemis ferruginea* (Fab.) (Odonata:Libellulidae). Folia Entomologica Mexicana 59:11-24.

Paulson, D.R. 1966. The dragonflies (Odonata:Anisoptera) of southern Florida. PhD. Dissertation, Univ. of Miami. 603 pp.

Paulson, D.R. 1966. New records of Bahamian Odonata. Quart. J. Fla. Acad. Sci. 29:97-110.

Paulson, D.R. 1973. Temporal isolation in two species of dragonflies, *Epitheca sepia* (Gloyd,1933) and *E. stella* (Williamson,1911) (Anisoptera:Corduliidae). Odonatologica 2(2):115-119.

Reichholf, J. 1973. A migration of *Pantala flavescens* (Fabricius,1798) along the shore of Santa Catarina, Brazil (Anisoptera:Libellulidae). Odonatologica 2(2):121-124.

Robey, C.W. 1975. Observations on breeding behavior of *Pachydiplax longipennis* (Odonata:Libellulidae). Psyche 82:89-96.

Sherman, K.J. 1983. The adaptive significance of postcopulatory mate guarding in a dragonfly, *Pachydiplax longipennis*. Anim. Behav. 31:1107-1115.

Shiffer, C. 1985. Odonata, pp. 91-161 *in* Species of special concern in Pennsylvania, H.H. Genoways and F.J. Brenner, Eds., Special Pub. Carnegie Mus. Nat. Hist. 11:91-161.

Waage, J.K. 1986. Sperm displacement by two libellulid dragonflies with disparate copulation durations (Anisoptera). Odonatologica 15(4):429-444. [Calico Pennant *Celithemis elisa*, and Eastern Pondhawk *Erythemis simplicollis*]

Walker, E.M. 1958. The Odonata of Canada and Alaska Vol. 2. Univ. Toronto Press, 318 pp.

Walker, E.M., and P.S. Corbet. 1975. The Odonata of Canada and Alaska Vol. 3. Univ. Toronto Press, 307 pp.

Westfall, M.J.,Jr. 1960. The Odonata of the Bahama Islands, the West Indies. Amer. Mus. Novitates 2020:1-12.

148

Williams, F.X. 1937. Notes on the biology of *Gynacantha nervosa* (Aeschninae), a crepuscular dragonfly in Guatemala. Pan- Pacific Ent. 13(1-2):1-8.

Williamson, E.B. 1902. Additions to the Indiana list of dragonflies, with a few notes. No. II. Proc. Indiana Acad. Sci. for 1901:119-127.

Williamson, E.B. 1907. A collecting trip north of Sault Ste. Marie, Ontario. Ohio Nat. 7(7):129-148.

Williamson, E.B. 1922. Indiana Somatochloras again (Odonata,Libellulidae). Entomol. News 33:200-207. [Mocha Emerald, *Somatochlora linearis*]

Williamson, E.B. 1923. Notes on American species of *Triacanthagyna* and *Gynacantha*. Misc. Pub. Univ. Michigan Mus. Zool. 9:1-80.

Williamson, E.B. 1932. Two new species of *Stylurus* (Odonata- Gomphinae). Occ. Pap. Mus. Zool. Univ. Michigan 247:1-18. [Shining Clubtail, *Stylurus ivae*]

Young, A.M. 1967. The flying season and emergence period of *Anax junius* in Illinois (Odonata:Aeshnidae). Canadian Entomol. 99:886-889.

Young, A.M. 1980. Observations on feeding aggregations of *Orthemis ferruginea* (Fabricius) in Costa Rica (Anisoptera:Libellulidae). Odonatologica 9(4):325-328.

INDEX

NOTES

NOTES

FLORIDA

BAHAMAS

CUBA

CAYMAN IS.

JAMAICA

CENTRAL AMERICA